THE
MICHELIN
GUIDE

NORDIC COUNTRIES

DENMARK I FINLAND I ICELAND
NORWAY I SWEDEN

MICHELIN

Operakällaren, Stockholm • Jussi Särkilahti/Pastis, Helsinki (top)

DEAR READER,

We are delighted to introduce the sixth edition of the Michelin guide to the Nordic Countries – a guide to the best places to eat and stay in Denmark, Finland, Iceland, Norway and Sweden. Alongside restaurants and hotels in the main cities, we are also pleased to recommend a selection of our favourite places from smaller towns and villages.

→ *The guide caters for every type of visitor, from business traveller to holiday maker, and highlights the best establishments, from cosy bistros and intimate townhouses to celebrated restaurants and luxury hotels.*

→ *The Michelin inspectors are the eyes and ears of our readers and their anonymity is key to ensuring that they receive the same treatment as any other guest. Each year, they search for new establishments to add to the guide, and only the best make it through. Once the annual selection has been made, the 'best of the best' are then recognised with Michelin Stars ✿ and Bib Gourmands ⊕.*

→ *Restaurants – our readers' favourite part – appear at the front of each locality, with the hotels following afterwards. Restaurants are ordered according to the quality of their food, with the Stars and Bib Gourmands placed at the top, followed by the Plates ⊫○. Being chosen by the Michelin Inspectors for inclusion in the guide is a guarantee of quality in itself and the plate symbol highlights restaurants where you will get a good meal.*

→ *Our mission is to help you find the best restaurants and hotels on your travels. Please don't hesitate to contact us,as we are keen to hear your opinions on the establishments listed within these pages, as well as those you feel could be of interest for future editions.*

We trust you will enjoy travelling with the 2019 edition of our Nordic Countries guide.

CONTENTS

THE MICHELIN GUIDE'S COMMITMENTS

➡ ANONYMOUS INSPECTIONS

Our inspectors make regular and anonymous visits to restaurants and hotels to gauge the quality of products and services offered to an ordinary customer. They settle their own bill and may then introduce themselves and ask for more information about the establishment. Our readers' comments are also a valuable source of information, which we can follow up with a visit of our own.

➡ INDEPENDENCE

To remain totally objective for our readers, the selection is made with complete independence. Entry into the guide is free. All decisions are discussed with the Editor and our highest awards are considered at a European level.

foto@carstenmuller.com/G2O

→ SELECTION AND CHOICE

The guide offers a selection of the best restaurants and hotels in every category of comfort and price. This is only possible because all the inspectors rigorously apply the same methods.

→ ANNUAL UPDATES

All the practical information, classifications and awards are revised and updated every year to give the most reliable information possible.

→ CONSISTENCY

The criteria for the classifications are the same in every country covered by the MICHELIN guide.

→ THE SOLE INTENTION OF MICHELIN IS TO MAKE YOUR TRAVELS SAFE AND ENJOYABLE.

QUALITY OF COOKING - THE DISTINCTIONS

✿✿✿ THREE STARS
Exceptional cuisine, worth a special journey!
Our highest award is given for the superlative cooking of chefs at the peak of their profession. The ingredients are exemplary, the cooking is elevated to an art form and their dishes are often destined to become classics.

✿✿ TWO STARS
Excellent cooking, worth a detour!
The personality and talent of the chef and their team is evident in the expertly crafted dishes, which are refined, inspired and sometimes original.

✿ ONE STAR
High quality cooking, worth a stop!
Using top quality ingredients, dishes with distinct flavours are carefully prepared to a consistently high standard.

😋 BIB GOURMAND
Good quality, good value cooking
'Bibs' are awarded for simple yet skilful cooking.

ⵔO PLATE
Good cooking
Fresh ingredients, capably prepared: simply a good meal.

SEEK AND SELECT...

RESTAURANTS

Restaurants are listed by distinction.
Within each distinction category, they
are then ordered alphabetically.

🌼🌼🌼 **Three Stars:** Exceptional cuisine,
worth a special journey!

🌼🌼 **Two Stars:** Excellent cooking,
worth a detour!

🌼 **One Star:** High quality cooking,
worth a stop!

☺ **Bib Gourmand:** Good quality,
good value cooking

🍴 **Michelin Plate:** Good cooking

WHERE YOU ARE

Bottom of the page:
country and town.

On the side:
neighbourhood.

KADEAU COPENHAGEN 🌼🌼

▶ MODERN CUISINE • DESIGN • FASHIONABLE

Wildersgade 10B ✉ 1408 K PLAN: D3
🚇 Christianshavn
TEL. 33 25 22 23 – **www**.kadeau.dk
Closed 5 weeks July-August, 24-26 December, 1-2 January
and Sunday-Tuesday
Menu 1950 DKK (dinner only and Saturday lunch)
(tasting menu only) (booking essential)

Chef:
Nicolai Nørregaard

Specialities:
Hot and cold smoked salmon,
elderflower and tomato water.
Fire-baked celery root, honey and
wood ants. Grilled, dried and fresh
pumpkin with lavender.

You'll receive a warm welcome at this delightful restaurant, where the
open kitchen adds a sense of occasion to the sophisticated room. The
chefs have an innate understanding of how best to match fresh and
aged produce, and use their experience in preserving and fermenting
to add many elements to each dish.

CENTRE

KEY WORDS

If you are looking for a specific type of establishment,
these key words will help you make your choice more
quickly.

• **For restaurants,** the first word relates to the type of
cuisine and the second, to the atmosphere.

• **For hotels,** the first word explains the establishment
type (chain, business, luxury, etc.); the second
describes the décor (modern, stylish, design, etc.)
and sometimes a third will be used to complete
the picture.

LOCATING THE ESTABLISHMENT

Location and coordinates on the town plan, with main sights

HOTELS

Hotels are listed by comfort, from 🏨🏨🏨 to 🏨. Within each comfort category, they are then ordered alphabetically.
Red: our most delightful places

KURHOTEL SKODSBORG

LUXURY • SPA AND WELLNESS • CONTEMPORARY

≼ 🛏 🐕 ᴒ 🔲 🆂🅿🅰 🔁 ᴌ ᴊ 🅿

Skodsborg Strandvej 139 ✉ 2942
TEL. 45 58 58 00 – **www**.skodsborg.dk
83 rm 😴 – 🛉 1400/2300 DKK 🛉🛉 1700/2600 DKK – 2 suites
THE RESTAURANT BY KROUN – See restaurant listing

A grand hotel with a world-renowned spa; founded in 1898 and rejuvenated by a substantial facelift. Luxury bedrooms have a modern style; choose one with a balcony to make the most of the view across the Øresund Strait. Enjoy a cocktail on the rooftop terrace or a relaxed meal in the brasserie.

FACILITIES & SERVICES

🍽	Hotel with a restaurant
♿	Wheelchair access
🅰	Air conditioning (in all or part of the establishment)
🏮	Outside dining available
🆂🅿🅰 🔁 ᴌ	Spa · Sauna · Exercise room
🏊 🏊	Swimming pool: outdoor or indoor
🌳 🎾	Garden or park · Tennis court
🏢 🍴	Conference room · Private dining room
🎭	Restaurant offering lower priced theatre menus
🚗 🚙 🅿	Valet parking · Garage · Car park
🚫	Credit cards not accepted
Ⓜ	Nearest metro station

OTHER SPECIAL FEATURES

🍃	Peaceful establishment
≼	Great view
🍷	Particularly interesting wine list

DENMARK

pidjoe/iStock

STARS & BIB GOURMAND

COPENHAGEN

Denmark

Some cities overwhelm you, and give the impression that there's too much of them to take in. Not Copenhagen. Most of its key sights are neatly compressed within its central Slotsholmen 'island', an area that enjoyed its first golden age in the early seventeenth century in the reign of Christian IV, when it became a harbour of great consequence. It has canals on three sides and opposite the harbour is the area of Christianshavn, home of the legendary freewheeling 'free-town' community of Christiania. Further up from the centre are Nyhavn, the much-photographed canalside with brightly coloured

buildings where the sightseeing cruises leave from, and the elegant Frederiksstaden, whose wide streets contain palaces and museums. West of the centre is where Copenhageners love to hang out: the Tivoli Gardens, a kind of magical fairyland. Slightly more down-to-earth are the western suburbs of Vesterbro and Nørrebro, which were run-down areas given a street credible spit and polish for the 21C, and are now two of the trendiest districts. Once you've idled away some time in the Danish capital, you'll wonder why anyone might ever want to leave. With its waterfronts, quirky shops and cafés, the city presents a modern, user-friendly ambience – but it also boasts world class art collections, museums, and impressive parks, gardens and lakes, all of which bear the mark of an earlier time.

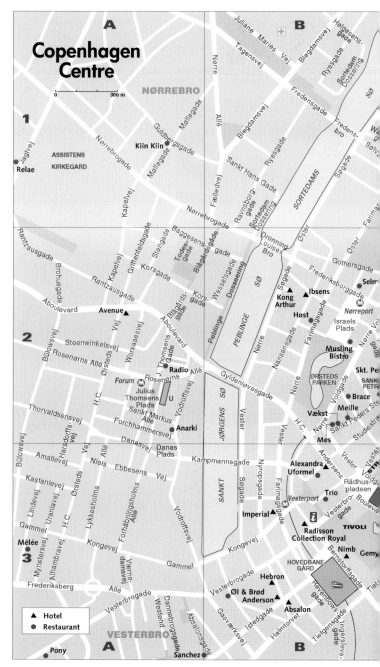

Copenhagen Centre

0 — 300 m

NØRREBRO

A

1

Jaghvej
Relæ

ASSISTENS
KIRKEGARD

Nørrebrogade

Guldbergsgade

Kiin Kiin

Møllegade

Mallegade

Kapelvej

Juliane Maries Vej

Tagensvej

Nørre

Blegdamsvej

Fælledvej

Sankt Hans Gade

Ravnsborg-gade

Nørrebrogade

Fredensgade

Ryesgade

Blegdamsvej

Helgesens-gade

Ryesgade

Sortedam Dossering

Sortedam Dossering

B

Fredens-bro

SORTEDAMS

Øster

W g
Solv

So

Østerg

Farima

Rantzausgade

Brohusgade

Kapelvej

Rantzausgade

Griffenfeldtsgade

Stengade

Todes-gade

Baggesensgade

Blågårdsgade

Korsgade

Wesselsgade

Dosseering

Øster

Farimag

Dronning Louises Bro

Gothersgade

Frederiksborggade

Selm

2

Aboulevard

Bülowsvej

Rosenørns Allé

Steenwinkelsvej

Worsaasvej

Kapelvej

Worsaasvej

Ø

Bülowsvej

H.C.

Thorvaldsensvej

Avenue ▲

Blågårds Plads

Korsgade

Aboulevard

J. Thomsens Gade

Radio ●

Rosenørns

Forum Ⓜ Allé

Julius Thomsens Plads

U

Sankt Markus Allé

Forchhammersvej

Anarki ●

Gyldenløvesgade

PEBLINGE

PEBLINGE SØ

Nørre

Vester

JØRGENS SØ

SØ

Nansensgade

Nørre

Farimagsgade

Kong Arthur ▲ ●Ibsens

Høst ●

Israels Plads

Nørreport Ⓜ

Musling Bistro

ØRSTEDS PARKEN

Vækst ●

Nørre

● Meille

Mes ●

● Brace

Nørre V

gade

Skt. Pe

SANK
PETR

Sankt Peders Str

Studiestr

3

Danasvej

Amalievej

Bülowsvej

Kastanievej

Lindevej

Uranievej

Niels Ebbesens Vej

Harsdorffs-vej

Ørsteds

H.C.

Lykkesholms Allé

Mêlée
●

Myrstersvej

Alhambravej

Gammel

Kongevej

Forhåbningsholms Allé

Frederiksberg Allé

Værne-damsvej

Danas Plads

Kampmannsgade

Nyropsgade

Søgade

SANKT

Vodroffsvej

Gammel

Vesterbrogade

Vesterbrogade

Dannebrogsgade

Westend

Absalonsgade

Farimagsgade

Alexandra ▲
Uformel ●

Vesterport Ⓜ

● Trio

Imperial ▲

Hebron ▲

Øl & Brød
Anderson ▲ ●

Gasværksvej

Istedgade

Andersens

Vesterbro

Vester

Vo
gade

Rådhus-pladsen

Boulevard

ℹ

Radisson
Collection Royal

HOVEDBANE
GÅRD

TIVOLI

Nimb ▲

● Absalon

Halmtorvet

Reventlows gade

Bernstorffsgade

Ingerslevs gade

Tietgensgade

Gemy

Tie

▲	Hotel
●	Restaurant

VESTERBRO

A

● Pony

B

Sanchez ●

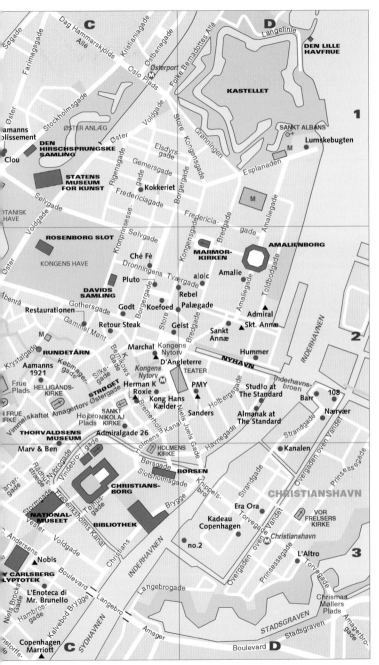

Søgade
Dag Hammarskjölds Allé
Farimagsgade
Kristianiagade
Langelinie
DEN LILLE HAVFRUE

Østbanegade
Folke Bernadottes Allé

Østerport Ⓜ
Oslo Plads

Øster
Stockholmsgade

ØSTER ANLÆG

KASTELLET

SANKT ALBANS
Lumskebugten

aamanns
olissement

DEN HIRSCHSPRUNGSKE SAMLING

Clou

Øster
Elsdyrsgade
Gemersgade
Rigensgade

Store Kongensgade
Grønningen
Esplanaden
Ⓜ

STATENS MUSEUM FOR KUNST

Fredericiagade
Kokkeriet

OTANISK HAVE

Sølvgade
Kronprinsesse-

Borgergade
Fredericia-gade
Ⓜ

Amaliegade
Bredgade

ROSENBORG SLOT

Sølvgade
Kongensgade

Toldbodgade

MARMOR-KIRKEN
AMALIENBORG

KONGENS HAVE

Ché Fè

Dronningens Tværgade

Amalie

Øster
benrå

Pluto
alolc
Rebel

Amaliegade

DAVIDS SAMLING
Gothersgade
Borgergade
Koefoed
Palægade

Admiral

Restaurationen
Godt
Geist
Skt. Annæ

Gammel Mønt
Retour Steak
Store
Bredgade
Sankt Annæ

INDERHAVNEN

Ⓜ
Marchal
Kongens Nytorv
Hummer

RUNDETÅRN
Benikows
Silke-gade

NYHAVN

Krystalgade
Købmager-gade
D'Angleterre

Aamanns 1921
Silke-gade
Kongens Nytorv
TEATER
Inderhavns-broen

Frue Plads
HELLIGÅNDS-KIRKE
Herman K
PMY
Studio at The Standard
Barr
108

STRØGET
Amagertorv Østergade
Roxie
Holbergsgade
Nærvær

R FRUE IRKE
Vimmelskaftet
SANKT NIKOLAJ KIRKE
Kong Hans Kælder
Bremerholm
Sanders
Almanak at The Standard

Strandgade

THORVALDSENS MUSEUM
Højbro Plads
Admiralgade 26
Niels Juels Gade
Havnegade

Marv & Ben
Holmens gade
HOLMENS KIRKE
Kanalen

Rådhus-stræde
Vindebro-gade
Nybrogade
Børsgade
BØRSEN

Overgaden oven Vandet
Prinsessegade

arver-gade
Stormgade
Frederiksholms Kanal
Tøjhus-gade
Slotsholmsgade

CHRISTIANS-BORG
Knippels-bro
Brygge

Strandgade
CHRISTIANSHAVN

Vester
NATIONAL-MUSEET
BIBLIOTHEK

Era Ora
Torvegade
VOR FRELSERS KIRKE

Andersens
Voldgade
Christians
Kadeau Copenhagen
Ⓜ Christianshavn

Nobis
Boulevard
no.2
Overgaden oven Vandet
L'Altro

W CARLSBERG LYPTOTEK

L'Enoteca di Mr. Brunello

Niels Brocks
Hambros-gade
Kalvebod Brygge
Langebro
INDERHAVNEN

Langebrogade
Prinsessegade
Torvegade

Chrismas Møllers Plads

Copenhagen Marriott

Amager
SYDHAVNEN

STADSGRAVEN
Stadsgraven
Amagerbro-gade

Boulevard

GERANIUM ✿✿✿

CREATIVE • DESIGN • ELEGANT

Per Henrik Lings Allé 4 (8th Fl), Parken National Stadium (3 km via Dag Hammaraskjölds Allé) ✉ 2100 Ø
TEL. 69 96 00 20 – www.geranium.dk
Closed 2 weeks Christmas, 2 weeks summer and Sunday-Tuesday
Menu 2500 DKK (surprise menu only) (booking essential)

Chef:
Rasmus Kofoed

Specialities:
Fjord shrimp tartlet, söl and pickled elderflower. Chicken with morels, green cabbage, sprouts, smoked chicken fat and hops. Beeswax and pollen ice cream with rhubarb.

Unusually located on the 8th floor of the National Football Stadium, this luxurious restaurant feels as if it is inviting the outside in with its panoramic park views. Modern techniques and the finest organic and biodynamic ingredients are used to create pure, beautiful and balanced dishes.

A|O|C ✿✿

MODERN CUISINE • ELEGANT • ROMANTIC

Dronningens Tværgade 2 ✉ 1302 K **PLAN: D2**
Ⓜ Kongens Nytorv
TEL. 33 11 11 45 – www.aoc.dk
Closed Christmas, 3 weeks July, 1 week February, 1 week October, Sunday and Monday
Menu 1700/2000 DKK (dinner only) (tasting menu only) (booking essential)

Chef:
Søren Selin

Specialities:
Scallop with fermented asparagus, dill and mussel cream. Quail, flowers and roasted potato skin. Burnt Jerusalem artichoke with caramel and hazelnut ice cream.

A spacious, simply decorated restaurant in the vaults of an eye-catching 17C building close to Nyhavn harbour; owned and run by an experienced sommelier and chef. Skilful, well-judged and, at times, playful cooking has a Danish heart and shows great originality, as well as a keen eye for detail, flavour and texture.

KADEAU COPENHAGEN ✿✿

MODERN CUISINE • DESIGN • FASHIONABLE

Wildersgade 10B ✉ 1408 K PLAN: D3
Ⓜ Christianshavn
TEL. 33 25 22 23 – www.kadeau.dk
Closed 5 weeks July-August, 24-26 December, 1-2 January
and Sunday-Tuesday
Menu 1950 DKK (dinner only and Saturday lunch)
(tasting menu only) (booking essential)

Chef:
Nicolai Nørregaard
Specialities:
Hot and cold smoked salmon,
elderflower and tomato water.
Fire-baked celery root, honey and
wood ants. Grilled, dried and fresh
pumpkin with lavender.

You'll receive a warm welcome at this delightful restaurant, where the
open kitchen adds a sense of occasion to the sophisticated room. The
chefs have an innate understanding of how best to match fresh and
aged produce, and use their experience in preserving and fermenting
to add many elements to each dish.

NOMA ✿✿

CREATIVE • RUSTIC • ELEGANT

Refshalevej 96 (East : 3.5 km. by Torvegade and Prinsessegade
D3) ✉ 1432
TEL. 32 96 32 97 – www.noma.dk
Closed 2 weeks mid-June, 2 weeks late September, first week
March and Saturday dinner-Monday
Menu 2500 DKK (dinner only and Saturday lunch)
(surprise menu only) (booking essential)

Chef:
René Redzepi
Specialities:
Fjord shrimps and summer
preserves with chicken 'skin'.
Celeriac shawarma. Flower pot
cake with roses and flowers.

An urban farm and restaurant with stunning lakeside views. Thought-
provoking seasonal menus offer seafood in spring, vegetables in
summer and game in autumn. Their considered and holistic approach
creates beautifully executed, original dishes packed with flavour and
delivered with confidence and pride.

CENTRE

ALOUETTE ఴ

MODERN CUISINE • TRENDY • DESIGN

Sturlasgade 14 (1st Floor) (through the arch) (Southwest :
2.5 km by H.C. Andersens Boulevard and Langebro off
Klaksvigsgade) ✉ 2300
Ⓜ Islands Brygge
TEL. 31 67 66 06 – www.restaurantalouette.dk
Closed Christmas and Sunday-Wednesday

Menu 695 DKK (dinner only) (surprise menu only) (booking essential)

Chef:
Nick Curtin

Specialities:
Embered pumpkin, caviar and
mulberry. Hegnsholt lamb,
chanterelles and new cabbage.
Plum wood smoked parfait and
plums.

Graffiti-covered corridors and a freight lift lead to this light, modern
restaurant in a former pencil factory. The confident chef understands
that less is more; combining a handful of top notch ingredients in
pared back, sublimely flavoured dishes. The open fire is used to great
effect.

CLOU ఴ

MODERN CUISINE • INTIMATE • NEIGHBOURHOOD

Øster Farimagsgade 8 ✉ 2100 K **PLAN: C1**
Ⓜ Nørreport
TEL. 91 92 72 30 – www.restaurant-clou.dk
Closed 22 December-2 January and Sunday-Tuesday

Menu 1600 DKK (dinner only) (tasting menu only) (booking
essential)

Chef:
Jonathan Berntsen

Specialities:
Hand-dived scallops and raw
cacao. 'Everything from the
quail'. Banana, brown butter and
liquorice.

An intimate, suburban restaurant where you can see into the basement
kitchen from the street. The tasting 'journey' is designed to match
6 carefully chosen, top quality wines. Creative dishes stimulate the
senses with their intense natural flavours and well-balanced contrasts
in texture and taste.

Alicon Vannini/Alouatta/Oak Food ApS • Restaurant Clou

ERA ORA ✿

ITALIAN • ELEGANT • INTIMATE

Overgaden Neden Vandet 33B ✉ 1414 K PLAN: D3
Ⓜ Christianshavn
TEL. 32 54 06 93 – www.era-ora.dk
Closed 24-26 December, 1 January, Easter Monday and Sunday
Menu 480/1280 DKK (tasting menu only) (booking essential)

Specialities:
Langoustine, cherry gel and langoustine cream. Ravioli of almond, lemon cream and amaranth. 'Sweet Italian Traditions'.

Set on a quaint cobbled street by the canal; a grand, long-standing restaurant with an enclosed rear terrace and a formal air. Complex, innovative dishes feature lots of different ingredients (many imported from Italy) and are often explorative in their approach. The wine cellar boasts over 90,000 bottles.

FORMEL B ✿

MODERN CUISINE • FASHIONABLE • DESIGN

Vesterbrogade 182-184, Frederiksberg (West : 2 km.) ✉ 1800 C
TEL. 33 25 10 66 – www.formelb.dk
Closed 24-26 December, 1-5 January and Sunday
Menu 900 DKK – Carte 420/575 DKK (dinner only)
(booking essential)

Chef:
Kristian Arpe-Møller

Specialities:
Langoustine à la nage with Danish vegetables. Pigeon with morels, truffles and asparagus. Sea buckthorn 'en surprise'.

The friendly staff help to create a relaxed environment at this appealing modern restaurant, with its tree pictures and dark wood branches; ask for a table on the lower level by the kitchen if you want to get close to the action. Complex, original small plates are crafted with an assured and confident touch.

KIIN KIIN ❀

THAI • EXOTIC DÉCOR • INTIMATE

Guldbergsgade 21 ✉ 2200 N PLAN: A1
TEL. 35 35 75 55 – www.kiin.dk
Closed Christmas and Sunday

Menu 495/975 DKK (dinner only) (tasting menu only)
(booking essential)

Specialities:
Frozen red curry with lobster. Stir-
fried beef with oyster sauce and
krachai. Pandan ice cream with
pistachio.

A charming restaurant, whose name means 'come and eat'. Start with
refined versions of street food in the moody lounge, then head for
the tasteful dining room decorated with golden Buddhas and fresh
flowers. Menus offer modern, personal interpretations of Thai dishes,
which have vibrant flavour combinations.

KOKKERIET ❀

MODERN CUISINE • INTIMATE • DESIGN

Kronprinsessegade 64 ✉ 1306 K PLAN: C1
TEL. 33 15 27 77 – www.kokkeriet.dk
Closed 24-26 December, 1 January and Sunday

Menu 900/1200 DKK – Carte 675/800 DKK (dinner only)
(booking essential)

Specialities:
Scallop, pumpkin and roses. Oxtail
with beetroot and horseradish.
Yoghurt, radish and walnut.

The kitchen takes Danish classics and adds its own modern
interpretation; dishes are fresh and colourful and all have their own
story. The focus is on the tasting menu; veggies and vegans are well
looked after. This very welcoming restaurant, once a corner shop, is
intimate and contemporary.

KONG HANS KÆLDER ✿

CLASSIC FRENCH • ELEGANT • INTIMATE   ✿ 🍽

Vingaardsstræde 6 ⊠ 1070 K **PLAN: C2**
Ⓜ Kongens Nytorv
TEL. 33 11 68 68 – www.konghans.dk
Closed 13-26 March, 17 April, 31 July-20 August, 23-27 December
and Sunday-Tuesday
Menu 1700 DKK – Carte 965/2065 DKK (dinner only)
(booking essential)

Specialities:
Scallops with smoked butter and
caviar. Black lobster 'à la Kong
Hans'. Chocolate soufflé and vanilla
ice cream.

A historic restaurant in a beautiful vaulted Gothic cellar in the heart
of the city. Richly flavoured, classic French cooking uses luxury
ingredients – signature dishes could include Danish Black lobster.
There's a 5 course tasting menu and Gueridon trolleys add a theatrical
element to proceedings.

MARCHAL ✿

MODERN CUISINE • ELEGANT • ROMANTIC   ✿ ♿ 🔊 A/C

D'Angleterre Hotel • Kongens Nytorv 34 ⊠ 1050 K **PLAN: C2**
Ⓜ Kongens Nytorv
TEL. 33 12 00 94 – www.marchal.dk
Menu 475 DKK (lunch) – Carte 435/1030 DKK

Specialities:
Squid with caviar and champagne
butter. Canard à la presse. Dark
chocolate mousse with cherries,
candied almonds and cherry
sorbet.

A stylish hotel restaurant overlooking the Square and named after
the man who founded the hotel in 1755. Refined, Nordic-style cooking
has a classical French base; menus offer a range of small plates – 3
is about the right amount. Dinner also includes an extensive caviar
collection.

108 ✿

MODERN CUISINE • NEIGHBOURHOOD • DESIGN

Strandgade 108 ✉ 1401 K PLAN: D2
Ⓜ Christianshavn
TEL. 32 96 32 92 – www.108.dk
Menu 1150 DKK – Carte 525/770 DKK (dinner only)
Closed 22-27 December and 1 January

Chef:
Kristian Baumann

Specialities:
Brown beech mushrooms with smoked egg yolk sauce. Lobster claw and raspberries. Wild blackcurrant sorbet with hazelnut milk

A former whale meat warehouse with floor to ceiling windows and water views; bare concrete and a semi-open kitchen give it a cool Nordic style. There's a Noma alumnus in the kitchen and plenty of pickled, cured and fermented ingredients on the 'no rules' menu, from which you pick as many dishes as you like.

RELÆ ✿

MODERN CUISINE • MINIMALIST • FASHIONABLE

Jægersborggade 41 ✉ 2200 N PLAN: A1
TEL. 36 96 66 09 – www.restaurant-relae.dk
Closed Christmas, 31 December, Sunday and Monday
Menu 475/895 DKK (dinner only and lunch Friday-Saturday) (surprise menu only) (booking essential)

Specialities:
White asparagus and buttermilk. Havervadgård lamb, dill and beach herbs. Birch, malt and juniper.

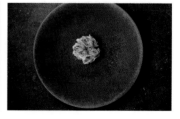

This modern, understated restaurant never stands still. The open kitchen provides a real sense of occasion and you can feel the passion of the chefs as they explain the dishes they are serving. 5 and 10 course surprise menus showcase produce grown on their farm. Dishes are intensely flavoured and unrestrained.

STUD!O AT THE STANDARD ✿

CREATIVE • FASHIONABLE • DESIGN ⇐ A/C

Havnegade 44 ✉ 1058 K **PLAN: D2**
Ⓜ Kongens Nytorv
TEL. 72 14 88 08 – www.thestandardcph.dk
Closed 2 weeks late summer, 22-26 December, 1-14 January,
Sunday, Monday and lunch Tuesday-Wednesday

Menu 700 DKK /1300 DKK (tasting menu only) (booking essential)

Specialities:
Churro, cheese and truffle.
Langoustine with passion fruit
and chilli. Gooseberry served
with coriander and olive oil.

The action at this stylishly understated restaurant is focused around
the open kitchen, with seating of varying heights so everyone has a
view. You'll notice subtle references to Chile – the chef's homeland –
in the various tasting menus. Precisely prepared, intensely flavoured
dishes are full of creativity.

L'ALTRO 🙂

ITALIAN • INTIMATE • TRADITIONAL DÉCOR A/C

Torvegade 62 ✉ 1400 K **PLAN: D3**
Ⓜ Christianshavn
TEL. 32 54 54 06 – www.laltro.dk
Closed 23-27 December, 1-9 January and Sunday

Menu 395/530 DKK (dinner only) (tasting menu only)
(booking essential)

A long-standing restaurant with a downstairs wine bar and a warm,
rustic style. It celebrates 'la cucina de la casa' – the homely Italian
spirit of 'mama's kitchen'. Regularly changing set menus feature tasty
family recipes from Umbria and Tuscany; dishes are appealing and
rely on top quality imported ingredients.

ANARKI 🕊

TRADITIONAL CUISINE • NEIGHBOURHOOD • BISTRO 🥢

Vodroffsvej 47 ✉ 1900 C **PLAN: A2**
Ⓜ Forum
TEL. 22 13 11 34 – www.restaurant-anarki.dk
Closed July, Christmas, Easter and Monday

Menu 395 DKK – Carte 275/435 DKK (dinner only)

An unassuming and proudly run neighbourhood bistro, set just over the water in Frederiksberg. The interesting menu of gutsy, flavourful dishes draws inspiration from all over the world, so expect to see words like ceviche, paella and burrata as well as bakskuld – with plenty of offal and some great wines.

ENOMANIA 🕊

ITALIAN • WINE BAR • SIMPLE 🥢 ⛲

Vesterbrogade 187 (West : 2.5 km) ✉ 1800 C
TEL. 33 23 60 80 – www.enomania.dk
Closed 21 December-6 January, 8-17 February, 9-13 and 18-22 April, 6 July-5 August, 12-21 October, Saturday-Monday and bank holidays

Menu 390 DKK – Carte 260/380 DKK (dinner only and lunch Thursday-Friday) (booking essential)

A simple, bistro-style restaurant near Frederiksberg Park – its name means 'Wine Mania'. The wine cellar comes with a table for tasting and there's an excellent list of over 600 bins, mostly from Piedmont and Burgundy. These are complemented by straightforward, tasty Italian dishes from a daily 4 course menu.

KØDBYENS FISKEBAR 🐡

SEAFOOD • SIMPLE • FASHIONABLE   🛜 🅿

Den Hvide Kødby, Flæsketorvet 100 (Southwest : 1 km via
Halmtorvet) ✉ 1711 V
TEL. 32 15 56 56 – www.fiskebaren.dk
Closed 24-26 December and 1 January

Menu 300 DKK (lunch) – Carte 300/565 DKK
(dinner only and lunch Friday-Sunday)

This buzzy, industrial-style restaurant is set – somewhat incongruously
– in a former butcher's shop in a commercial meat market. Menus
feature freshly prepared 'hot' and 'cold' seafood dishes which are
based around the latest catch, and oysters are a speciality. The
terrace is a popular spot come summer.

MARV & BEN 🐡

MODERN CUISINE • BISTRO • FASHIONABLE

Snaregade 4 ✉ 1205 K   **PLAN: C2/3**
Ⓜ Kongens Nytorv
TEL. 33 91 01 91 – www.marvogben.dk
Closed Christmas

Menu 400/600 DKK – Carte 290/385 DKK (dinner only)

The young owners bring plenty of enthusiasm to this little restaurant,
where dining is split over two dimly lit floors. Organic produce
features in seasonal dishes which display purity and depth of flavour.
Choose 'Four Favourites' (4 courses), 'Almost Everything' (6 courses)
or from the à la carte.

MÊLÉE 🐶

FRENCH • FRIENDLY • BISTRO

Martensens Allé 16 ✉ 1828 C **PLAN: A3**
Ⓜ Frederiksberg
TEL. 35 13 11 34 – www.melee.dk
Closed Christmas, Easter and Sunday

Menu 395 DKK – Carte 335/445 DKK (dinner only)
(booking essential)

A bustling neighbourhood bistro with a friendly, laid-back atmosphere; run by an experienced team. Modern, country-style cooking is French-based but has Danish influences; menus may be concise but portions are generous and flavours are bold. An excellent range of wines from the Rhône Valley accompany.

MUSLING BISTRO 🐶

SEAFOOD • BISTRO • FASHIONABLE   A/C

Linnésgade 14 ✉ 1361 K **PLAN: B2**
Ⓜ Nørreport
TEL. 34 10 56 56 – www.muslingbistro.dk
Closed 24-26 December, 1 January, Sunday and Monday

Carte 315/495 DKK

A relaxed bar-cum-bistro next to the Nørrebro food market – find a space at the black ash counter, grab your cutlery from one of the pots, and choose from the list of modern craft beers and unusual wines. Fantastic fresh seafood is to the fore on the concise menu, and service is swift and efficient.

PLUTO 🎭

MEDITERRANEAN CUISINE • BISTRO • RUSTIC

Borgergade 16 ⊠ 1300 K **PLAN: C2**
Ⓜ Kongens Nytorv
TEL. 33 16 00 16 – www.restaurantpluto.dk
Closed 24-25 December and 1 January

Menu 475 DKK – Carte 305/430 DKK (dinner only)

An appealing restaurant in a residential area, with concrete pillars and an intentionally 'unfinished' feel – sit at wooden tables, at the long metal bar or at communal marble-topped tables. The enticing menu is made up of small plates; cooking is rustic, unfussy and flavoursome.

PMY 🎭

SOUTH AMERICAN • FRIENDLY • TRENDY

Tordenskjoldsgade 11 ⊠ 1055 K **PLAN: D2**
Ⓜ Kongens Nytorv
TEL. 50 81 00 02 – www.restaurant-pmy.com
Closed July, 23-27 December, 1-7 January, Sunday and Monday

Menu 275/395 DKK (dinner only)
(booking essential)

Start with some snacks and a cocktail at this fun, laid-back restaurant, before moving on to fresh, zingy dishes bursting with Latin American flavours. Potato, Maize and Yuca feature highly on the small menu, which lists tasty, good value dishes from Peru, Mexico and Venezuela.

REBEL ☺

SMØRREBRØD • BISTRO • FASHIONABLE   ☺☺

MODERN CUISINE • BISTRO • FASHIONABLE

Store Kongensgade 52 ✉ 1264 K PLAN: C/D2
Ⓜ Kongens Nytorv
TEL. 33 32 32 09 – www.restaurantrebel.dk
Closed 22 July-4 August, 2 weeks Christmas, Sunday and Monday
Carte 315/525 DKK (dinner only)

Located in a busy part of the city; a simply decorated, split-level restaurant with closely set tables and a buzzy vibe. Choose 3 or 4 dishes from the list of 12 starter-sized options; cooking is modern and refined, and relies largely on Danish produce. The atmospheric lower floor is often used for parties.

SELMA ☺

SMØRREBRØD • SIMPLE • FRIENDLY

Rømersgade 20 ✉ 1362 K PLAN: B2
TEL. 93 10 72 03 – www.selmacopenhagen.dk
Closed 3 weeks July, 24-25 December, New Year and dinner
Sunday-Tuesday
Menu 325/345 DKK – Carte 300/450 DKK

A sweet homely place, named after the owner-chef's daughter and run by a friendly young team. Lunchtime smørrebrød are modern in style whilst respecting tradition; dinner dispenses with the rye and sourdough bases to create dishes ideal for sharing. Excellent selection of craft beers.

AAMANNS ETABLISSEMENT 🍴

DANISH • BISTRO • COSY

Øster Farimagsgade 12 ✉ 2100 Ø **PLAN: C1**
Ⓜ Nørreport
TEL. 20 80 52 02 – www.aamanns.dk
Closed 3 weeks July, 24-25 and 31 December, 1 January and dinner
Sunday-Tuesday

Carte 145/365 DKK

The perfect setting for classic smørrebrød is this cosy, contemporary
restaurant. Choose one of their fixed selections which feature their
signature herrings and fried plaice – and order their homemade snaps,
flavoured with handpicked herbs to accompany.

AAMANNS 1921 🍴

MODERN CUISINE • BRASSERIE • DESIGN   A/C

Niels Hemmingsens Gade 19-21 ✉ 1153 K **PLAN: C2**
Ⓜ Kongens Nytorv
TEL. 20 80 52 04 – www.aamanns.dk
Closed 24-25 and 31 December, 1 January and dinner Sunday-
Monday

Menu 290/390 DKK – Carte 235/385 DKK

An appealing restaurant with original stone arches. Lunch sees
traditional smørrebrød, while dinner focuses on modern dishes. They
grind and mill their own flours, marinate their herring for 6-12 months
and gather the herbs for their snaps.

ADMIRALGADE 26 🍴

MODERN CUISINE • INTIMATE • COSY

Admiralgade 26 ✉ 1066 K PLAN: C2
Ⓜ Kongens Nytorv
TEL. 33 33 79 73 – www.admiralgade26.dk
Closed 23-26 and 31 December, 1-3 January, Sunday and bank holidays
Menu 550 DKK (dinner) – Carte 275/395 DKK

This historic house dates from 1796 and sits in one of the oldest parts of the city. It's a relaxed place – a mix of wine bar, café and bistro – and, alongside an appealing modern menu, offers around 4,000 frequently changing wines.

ALMANAK AT THE STANDARD 🍴

MODERN CUISINE • FASHIONABLE • CHIC

Havnegade 44 ✉ 1058 K PLAN: D2
Ⓜ Kongens Nytorv
TEL. 72 14 88 08 – www.thestandardcph.dk
Closed 24 December, 1-2 January and Monday
Menu 575 DKK (dinner) – Carte 295/580 DKK

A chic restaurant on the ground floor of an impressive art deco customs building on the waterfront. At lunch, it's all about smørrebrød, while dinner sees a concise menu of updated Danish classics. An open kitchen adds to the theatre.

AMALIE ⁏○

SMØRREBRØD • INTIMATE • RUSTIC

Amaliegade 11 ✉ 1256 K **PLAN: D2**
Ⓜ Kongens Nytorv
TEL. 33 12 88 10 – www.restaurantamalie.dk
Closed 3 weeks July, Christmas, Easter, Sunday and bank holidays
Menu 279 DKK – Carte 265/322 DKK (lunch only)
(booking essential)

A charming 18C townhouse by Amalienborg Palace, with two tiny, cosy rooms filled with old paintings and elegant porcelain. The Danish menu offers a large choice of smørrebrød, herring, salmon and salads. Service is warm and welcoming.

AMASS ⁏○

DANISH • MINIMALIST • FRIENDLY

Refshalevej 153 (3 km via Torvgade and Prinsessgade) ✉ 1432
TEL. 43 58 43 30 – www.amassrestaurant.com
Closed January, 1 week summer, Christmas, Sunday, Monday and lunch September-April
Menu 695/995 DKK (dinner only) (booking essential)

A large restaurant just outside the city. It has an urban, industrial feel courtesy of graffitied concrete walls and huge windows overlooking the old docks. Prices and the authenticity of ingredients are key; cooking is modern Danish.

BARR ⅱ○

MODERN CUISINE • TRENDY • RUSTIC

Strandgade 93 ✉ 1401 K PLAN: D2
Ⓜ Christianshavn
TEL. 32 96 32 93 – www.restaurantbarr.com
Closed 23-26 and 31 December, 1 January and 1 November
Menu 600 DKK – Carte 385/545 DKK
(dinner only and lunch Friday-Sunday) (booking essential)

A laid-back quayside restaurant with wood-clad walls. Its name means 'Barley' and it has an amazing array of cask and bottled beers (some custom-brewed), along with beer pairings to match the food. Intensely flavoured, rustic dishes have classic Nordic roots but are taken to new heights; the sweet cake is a must.

BRACE ⅱ○

ITALIAN • ELEGANT • FASHIONABLE

Teglgårdstræde 8a ✉ 1452 K PLAN: B2
Ⓜ Nørreport
TEL. 28 88 20 01 – www.restaurantbrace.dk
Closed 1-21 January, 24-26 December, Easter and Sunday
Menu 515/775 DKK – Carte 325/495 DKK (dinner only and lunch Friday-Saturday) (booking essential)

The name of this smart restaurant, set in the heart of the city, refers to the building's external structure and to the solidarity of the tight-knit team. Dishes are a fusion of Danish and Italian, and come with colourful modern twists.

CHÉ FÈ ⅃⃝

ITALIAN • SIMPLE • NEIGHBOURHOOD

Borgergade 17a ⊠ 1300 K **PLAN: C2**
Ⓜ Kongens Nytorv
TEL. 33 11 17 21 – www.chefe.dk
Closed 23-26 December, 10 June, Easter Monday and Sunday

Menu 435 DKK – Carte 375/465 DKK (dinner only)
(booking essential)

An unassuming façade conceals an appealing trattoria with pastel
hues and coffee sack curtains. Menus offer authentic Italian classics,
including homemade pastas; virtually all ingredients are imported
from small, organic producers.

L' ENOTECA DI MR. BRUNELLO ⅃⃝

ITALIAN • ELEGANT • NEIGHBOURHOOD   🍇

Rysensteensgade 16 ⊠ 1564 K **PLAN: C3**
Ⓜ København Hovedbane Gård
TEL. 33 11 47 20 – www.lenoteca.dk
Closed July-early August, Easter, Christmas, Sunday, Monday and
bank holidays

Menu 495/695 DKK – Carte 560/595 DKK (dinner only)

Tucked away near the Tivoli Gardens and run by passionate,
experienced owners. Refined, classic Italian cooking uses quality
produce imported from Italy. The good value Italian wine list has
over 150 different Brunello di Montalcinos.

FREDERIKS HAVE ⅈ○

DANISH • NEIGHBOURHOOD • FAMILY

Smallegade 41, (entrance on Virginiavej) (West : 3 km. via Gammel Kongevej) ⊠ 2000 F
Ⓜ Fasanvej St.
TEL. 38 88 33 35 – www.frederikshave.dk
Closed Christmas, Easter and Sunday

Menu 295/400 DKK – Carte 355/565 DKK

A sweet two-roomed neighbourhood restaurant hidden just off the main street in a residential area. Sit inside – surrounded by flowers and vivid local art – or outside, on the terrace. Good value menus offer a mix of traditional Danish and French dishes.

GEIST ⅈ○

MODERN CUISINE • DESIGN • TRENDY

Kongens Nytorv 8 ⊠ 1050 K **PLAN: C2**
Ⓜ Kongens Nytorv
TEL. 33 13 37 13 – www.restaurantgeist.dk
Closed 24-26 December and 1-2 January

Carte 370/560 DKK

A lively, fashionable restaurant with an open kitchen and floor to ceiling windows overlooking the square. Choose the large counter at the front, or more intimate dining at the rear. The cleverly crafted dishes display a light touch; 4 should suffice.

GEMYSE 🍴⚪

MODERN CUISINE • RUSTIC • ROMANTIC

Nimb Hotel • Tivoli Gardens, Bernstoffsgade 5 ✉ 1572 V **PLAN: B3**
Ⓜ København Hovedbane Gård
TEL. 88 70 00 80 – www.nimb.dk
Closed 25 February-3 April, 23 September-10 October,
4-15 November and 1-2 January
Menu 550 DKK – Carte 280/480 DKK

This delightful vegetable-orientated restaurant – part of the Nimb hotel – sits in the heart of Tivoli Gardens (when they are open, admission must be paid). It comes complete with a greenhouse and raised beds where they grow much of the produce. Dishes are well-prepared, attractively presented and very tasty.

GODT 🍴⚪

CLASSIC CUISINE • FRIENDLY • FAMILY

Gothersgade 38 ✉ 1123 K **PLAN: C2**
Ⓜ Kongens Nytorv
TEL. 33 15 21 22 – www.restaurant-godt.dk
Closed mid July-mid August, Christmas-New Year, Easter, Sunday, Monday and bank holidays
Menu 520/680 DKK (dinner only) (tasting menu only)

2019 is the 25th anniversary of this family run restaurant which seats just 20 on two levels. The cooking is underpinned by a strong classical base and the dishes on the daily changing menu are satisfying and full of flavour. Old WWII shells act as candle holders.

HØST ⅰ○

MODERN CUISINE • FRIENDLY • RUSTIC

Nørre Farimagsgade 41 ⊠ 1364 K PLAN: B2
Ⓜ Nørreport
TEL. 89 93 84 09 – www.cofoco.dk/restauranter/hoest
Closed 24 December and 1 January

Menu 350/450 DKK (dinner only)

A busy neighbourhood bistro with fun staff and a lively atmosphere; sit in the Garden Room. The great value monthly set menu comprises 3 courses but comes with lots of extras. Modern Nordic cooking is seasonal and boldly flavoured.

HUMMER ⅰ○

SEAFOOD • FRIENDLY • SIMPLE

Nyhavn 63a ⊠ 1051 K PLAN: D2
Ⓜ Kongens Nytorv
TEL. 33 33 03 39 – www.restauranthummer.dk
Closed 23-27 December and Monday-Tuesday October-April

Menu 395 DKK – Carte 290/610 DKK

Lobster is the mainstay of the menu at this restaurant, situated among the brightly coloured buildings on the famous Nyhavn strip. Enjoy a meal on the sunny terrace or in the modish, nautically styled dining room.

KANALEN ⅋○

DANISH • BISTRO • COSY

Wilders Plads 2 ⊠ 1403 K PLAN: D3
Ⓜ Christianshavn
TEL. 32 95 13 30 – www.restaurant-kanalen.dk
Closed Christmas-New Year, Easter, 9-10 June,
Sunday and bank holidays
Menu 250/655 DKK – Carte 395/780 DKK (booking essential)

Find a spot on the delightful canalside terrace of this quaint, shack-like building – formerly the Harbour Police office – and watch the boats bobbing up and down as you eat. Alongside classic Danish flavours you'll find some light French and Asian touches; for dessert, the 'flødeboller' is a must.

KIIN KIIN VEVE ⅋○

VEGETARIAN • DESIGN • CONTEMPORARY DÉCOR

Dampfærgevej 7 (North : 2.5 km by Store Kongensgade and Folke
Bernadottes Allé) ⊠ 2100 Ø
TEL. 51 22 59 55 – www.veve.dk
Closed Christmas and Sunday-Tuesday
Menu 750 DKK (dinner only) (tasting menu only)
(booking essential)

A former bread factory houses this chic restaurant which serves sophisticated vegetarian cuisine. The 6 course tasting menu revolves around the seasons and offers some imaginative combinations. Wine and juice pairings accompany.

Harry Nielsen/Kanalen - Kanalen • Kiin Kiin Veve

KOEFOED ⁑○

MODERN CUISINE • INTIMATE • ROMANTIC

Landgreven 3 ⊠ 1301 K PLAN: C2
Ⓜ Kongens Nytorv
TEL. 56 48 22 24 – www.restaurant-koefoed.dk
Closed 26-December-1 January, Sunday and Monday

Menu 295/495 DKK – Carte 425/500 DKK
(booking essential at dinner)

An intimate collection of rooms in an old coal cellar, where everything from the produce to the glassware celebrates Bornholm island. Modern cooking is accompanied by an impressive range of bordeaux wines. Lunch sees reinvented smørrebrød.

LUMSKEBUGTEN ⁑○

TRADITIONAL CUISINE • COSY • CLASSIC DÉCOR

Esplanaden 21 ⊠ 1263 K PLAN: D1
TEL. 33 15 60 29 – www.lumskebugten.dk
Closed 3 weeks July, Christmas, Easter and Sunday

Menu 375/485 DKK – Carte 300/630 DKK

A traditional quayside restaurant with period décor, charming staff and a warm ambience. Lunch means classic Danish dishes with plenty of herrings and smørrebrød; dinner offers a menu of traditional dishes with a Danish heart, like fried fish on the bone or Danish rib-eye steaks.

Koefoed • Lumskebugten

MEILLE ⚫🍴

MODERN CUISINE • BISTRO • FASHIONABLE ⒶⒸ

Sankt Peders Stræde 24a ✉ 1453 K **PLAN: B2**
Ⓜ Nørreport
TEL. 53 65 14 53 – www.restaurant-meille.dk
Closed Christmas-New Year, Monday and lunch Tuesday-
Wednesday
Menu 195/345 DKK – Carte lunch 200/250 DKK
(booking essential at dinner)

 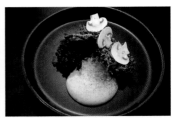

Sister to Mes round the corner, 'Us' is a busy bistro with shelves full
of cookbooks, wine bottles and jars of preserved, fermented and
marinating produce. Lunch offers a classic smørrebrød selection;
dinner sees a 3 or 5 course set menu of creative modern Nordic dishes
with a rustic edge.

MES ⚫🍴

DANISH • INTIMATE • FRIENDLY

Jarmers Plads 1 ✉ 1551 V **PLAN: B2**
Ⓜ Nørreport
TEL. 25 36 51 81 – www.restaurant-mes.dk
Closed 24-26 December and Sunday
Menu 350 DKK (dinner only) (tasting menu only)
(booking essential)

A sweet little restaurant run by a tight-knit team. The frequently
changing set menu lists classic dishes – some of which are pepped
up with modern techniques. A 120 year old German cooling cabinet
plays host to the wines.

MIELCKE & HURTIGKARL ⏹️

CREATIVE • ELEGANT • EXOTIC DÉCOR

Runddel 1 (West : 2.5 km. via Veseterbrogade and Frederiksberg
Allé) ✉ 2000 C
TEL. 38 34 84 36 – www.mhcph.com
Closed 3 weeks Christmas, Sunday and Monday

Menu 800/950 DKK (dinner only) (booking essential)

Set in a delightful spot in Frederiksberg Gardens, its walls painted
with garden scenes, is this charming 1744 orangery with a fire-lit
terrace. Dishes come from around the globe, with Asian influences to
the fore – and an amazing array of herbs from the gardens.

NÆRVÆR ⏹️

MODERN CUISINE • DESIGN • MINIMALIST   ♿ 🅰️🅲️

Krøyers Plads, Strandgade 87c ✉ 1401 K PLAN: D2
🅜 Christianshavn
TEL. 77 30 12 11 – www.naervaer.dk
Closed 26 December and Sunday-Tuesday

Menu 1200 DKK (dinner only) (tasting menu only)
(booking essential)

Close to the water in Christianshavn, this is half wine bar, half
counter restaurant; its bare concrete walls allowing no distraction
from watching the chefs at work. 7 course monthly changing menu
of modern, original dishes; some show evidence of the owner-chef's
French roots.

NO.2 ⫛○

MODERN CUISINE • DESIGN • FASHIONABLE ← 🏠 AC

Nicolai Eigtveds Gade 32 ⊠ 1402 K PLAN: D3
Ⓜ Christianshaven
TEL. 33 11 11 68 – www.nummer2.dk
Closed 3 weeks July, Christmas, Easter, Saturday lunch and Sunday
Menu 325/475 DKK – Carte 300/425 DKK

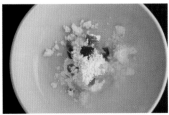

Set among smart offices and apartments on the edge of the dock is this elegant restaurant; a sister to a|o|c. Fresh, flavoursome dishes focus on quality Danish ingredients – highlights include the cured hams, cheeses and ice creams.

ØL & BRØD ⫛○

MODERN CUISINE • NEIGHBOURHOOD • COSY

Viktoriagade 6 ⊠ 1620 V PLAN: B3
Ⓜ København Hovedbane Gård
TEL. 33 31 44 22 – www.ologbrod.com
Closed Monday and dinner Tuesday-Wednesday
Menu 300/400 DKK – Carte 275/490 DKK (booking essential)

A cosy, hip neighbourhood restaurant where the emphasis is as much on aquavit and craft beers as it is on the refined and flavourful modern food. Lunch sees smørrebrød taken to a new level, while dinner offers a choice of 3 or 6 courses.

PALÆGADE 🍴○

SMØRREBRØD • FRIENDLY • SIMPLE

Palægade 8 ✉ 1261 K PLAN: C/D2
Ⓜ Kongens Nytorv
TEL. 70 82 82 88 – www.palaegade.dk
Closed 24-26 December, 1-4 January and Sunday dinner
Menu 450 DKK – Carte 260/525 DKK

More than 40 classic smørrebrød are available at lunch – with plenty
of local beers and snaps to accompany them. Things become more
formal in the evenings, when they serve highly seasonal dishes in a
traditional Northern European style.

PONY 🍴○

DANISH • BISTRO • NEIGHBOURHOOD

Vesterbrogade 135 ✉ 1620 V PLAN: A3
TEL. 33 22 10 00 – www.ponykbh.dk
Closed 6 weeks July-August, 1 week Christmas and Monday
Menu 425/485 DKK (dinner only) (booking essential)

A buzzy restaurant with chatty service; sit on high stools by the
kitchen or in the retro dining room. Choose from the fixed price menu
or try the more adventurous 4 course 'Pony Kick'. Refined, modern
cooking has a nose-to-tail approach.

RADIO ⅋O

MODERN CUISINE • MINIMALIST • NEIGHBOURHOOD

Julius Thomsens Gade 12 ⊠ 1632 V PLAN: A2
Ⓜ Forum
TEL. 25 10 27 33 – www.restaurantradio.dk
Closed 3 weeks summer, 2 weeks Christmas-New Year, Sunday and
Monday

Menu 350 DKK (dinner only and lunch Friday-Saturday)
(tasting menu only) (booking essential)

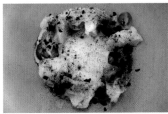

An informal restaurant with an unfussy urban style, wood-clad walls
and cool anglepoise lighting. Oft-changing menus feature full-
flavoured, good value dishes and use organic ingredients grown in the
restaurant's nearby fields. Pick 3 or 5 dishes from the five understated
choices.

RESTAURATIONEN ⅋O

CLASSIC CUISINE • CHIC • ROMANTIC   ⅋

Møntergade 19 ⊠ 1116 K PLAN: C2
Ⓜ Kongens Nytorv
TEL. 33 14 94 95 – www.restaurationen.dk
Closed 29 June-26 August, 21 December-6 January, 14-22 April,
Sunday and Monday
Menu 635 DKK (dinner only)

This friendly restaurant is over a quarter of a century old, and run by
a well-known chef who also owns the next door wine bar. The dining
room displays some impressive contemporary art and the modern
Danish dishes are created with good quality local produce.

RETOUR STEAK ⚔️🍴

MEATS AND GRILLS • BISTRO • FRIENDLY

Ny Østergade 21 ✉ 1101 K **PLAN: C2**
Ⓜ Kongens Nytorv
TEL. 33 16 17 19 – www.retoursteak.dk
Closed 25 December and 1 January

Carte 240/625 DKK (dinner only) (booking essential)

A relaxed, informal restaurant with a stark white interior and contrasting black furnishings. A small menu offers simply prepared grills, good quality American rib-eye steaks and an affordable selection of wines.

ROXIE ⚔️🍴

MODERN CUISINE • DESIGN • FASHIONABLE   🏠 [A/C]

Herman K Hotel • Bremerholm 6 ✉ 1069 K **PLAN: C2**
Ⓜ Kongens Nytorv
TEL. 53 89 10 69 – www.roxie.dk
Closed 24-25 December, 1 January and lunch Monday-Thursday

Menu 400 DKK (lunch) – Carte 465/600 DKK (booking essential at dinner)

Little sister to Kadeau is this chic, industrial style restaurant set over three floors of a boutique hotel. The modern bistro dishes use lots of pickled, fermented and preserved produce and are full of interesting textures and flavours. Relaxed but professional service from a knowledgeable team.

SANCHEZ ⅡO

MEXICAN • NEIGHBOURHOOD • BISTRO

Istedgade 60 ✉ 1650 **PLAN: A/B3**
Ⓜ København Hovedbane Gård
TEL. 31 11 66 40 – www.lovesanchez.com
Closed Tuesday-Wednesday

Menu 375 DKK – Carte 200/300 DKK (dinner only and lunch
Saturday-Sunday) (booking essential)

Neighbourhood cantina offering Mexican small plates, powerful
flavours and a lot of fun; grab a seat at the counter, order a Mezcal and
watch the chefs at work. The best choice is the 'favourite servings',
which is five dishes selected by the kitchen. Come for brunch at the
weekend.

SANKT ANNÆ ⅡO

SMØRREBRØD • COSY • CLASSIC DÉCOR

Sankt Annæ Plads 12 ✉ 1250 K **PLAN: D2**
Ⓜ Kongens Nytorv
TEL. 33 12 54 97 – www.restaurantsanktannae.dk
Closed 15 July-4 August, Christmas-New Year, Sunday and bank
holidays

Carte 220/440 DKK (lunch only) (booking essential)

An attractive terraced building with a traditional, rather quaint
interior. There's a seasonal à la carte and a daily blackboard menu:
prices can vary so check before ordering. The lobster and shrimp –
fresh from local fjords – are a hit.

TRIO ⁇○

MODERN CUISINE • DESIGN • FASHIONABLE ⁇ ⁇ A/C ⁇

Axel Towers (9th Floor), Jernbanegade 11 ⊠ 1608 V **PLAN: B3**
Ⓜ København Hovedbane Gård
TEL. 44 22 74 74 – www.restauranttrio.dk
Closed 3 weeks July, Christmas, Easter and Sunday
Menu 400/675 DKK – Carte 350/555 DKK

The highest restaurant in the city is located on floors 9 and 10 of the striking Axel Towers building; enjoy a cocktail while taking in the view. Accomplished dishes take their influences from both classic French and modern Nordic cuisine.

UFORMEL ⁇○

MODERN CUISINE • FASHIONABLE • TRENDY   A/C ⁇

Studiestraede 69 ⊠ 1554 V **PLAN: B3**
Ⓜ Vesterport
TEL. 70 99 9111 – www.uformel.dk
Closed 23-28 December and 1 January

Menu 800 DKK – Carte 360/600 DKK (dinner only)
(booking essential)

The informal sister of Formel B, with gold table-tops, black cutlery, a smart open kitchen and a cocktail bar (a lively spot at the weekend!) Dishes are tasting plates and all are the same price; 4-6 is about the right amount.

VÆKST ⚫🍴

MODERN CUISINE • RUSTIC • TRENDY   ♿ 🛜 A/C

Sankt Peders Stræde 34 ✉ 1453 PLAN: B2
Ⓜ Nørreport
TEL. 38 41 27 27 – www.cofoco.dk/en/restaurants/vaekst/
Closed 24 December, 1 January and Sunday lunch
Menu 325 DKK – Carte 375/435 DKK

Dining outside 'inside' is the theme here, and you'll find plants, garden furniture and a full-sized greenhouse at the centre of the room. Interesting Danish cooking follows the seasons and is light, stimulating and full of flavour.

D'ANGLETERRE   🏠

LUXURY • HISTORIC • CONTEMPORARY

☂ ♿ 🖼 🈺 🛏 🧖 A/C 🧖‍♀️

Kongens Nytorv 34 ✉ 1050 K PLAN: C2
Ⓜ Kongens Nytorv
TEL. 33 12 00 95 – www.dangleterre.com
92 rm – 👤 3350/4350 DKK 👥 4750/5850 DKK, ☕ 325 DKK – 30 suites
MARCHAL ✽ – See restaurant listing

A smartly refurbished landmark hotel dating back over 250 years. Well-equipped bedrooms come in various shapes and sizes; it's worth paying the extra for a Royal Square view. Unwind in the basement spa or the chic champagne bar.

COPENHAGEN MARRIOTT

LUXURY • BUSINESS • MODERN

Kalvebod Brygge 5 ⊠ 1560 V PLAN: C3
TEL. 88 33 99 00 – www.copenhagenmarriott.dk
402 rm – ♦ 1900/5000 DKK ♦♦ 1900/5000 DKK, ☕ 230 DKK
– 9 suites

A striking waterfront hotel; take in the views from the terrace or from the lounge-bar's floor to ceiling windows. Bright, spacious bedrooms are handsomely appointed and afford canal or city views. The popular American grill restaurant offers steaks, chops and seafood, and has a lively open kitchen.

SKT. PETRI

BUSINESS • BOUTIQUE HOTEL • MODERN

Krystalgade 22 ⊠ 1172 K PLAN: B2
Ⓜ Nørreport
TEL. 33 45 91 00 – www.sktpetri.com
288 rm – ♦ 1215/2200 DKK ♦♦ 1490/3650 DKK, ☕ 126 DKK

Much of this 7-storey building is listed; it's been stylishly fitted out and displays modern Danish art. The basement restaurant serves international cuisine and there's a nice garden courtyard with a wood-burning stove. Bedrooms are state-of-the-art and some have views over the city spires.

NIMB

LUXURY • DESIGN • ROMANTIC

Bernstorffsgade 5 ⊠ 1577 V **PLAN: B3**
Ⓜ København Hovedbane Gård
TEL. 88 70 00 00 – www.nimb.dk
38 rm – ♦ 2800/3000 DKK ♦♦ 3900/5400 DKK, ⌂ 195 DKK – 12 suites
GEMYSE – See restaurant listing

An ornate, Moorish-style building dating from 1909, situated in Tivoli Gardens. Smart bedrooms are sympathetically designed and well-equipped – most overlook the gardens. Eat in the lively bar and grill, the formal brasserie or vegetable-orientated Gemyse. The rustic wine bar offers over 2,000 bottles – and you can enjoy Danish open sandwiches and snaps in Fru Nimb.

ADMIRAL

BUSINESS • HISTORIC • MODERN

Toldbodgade 24-28 ⊠ 1253 K **PLAN: D2**
Ⓜ Kongens Nytorv
TEL. 33 74 14 14 – www.admiralhotel.dk
366 rm – ♦ 845/1945 DKK ♦♦ 1075/3995 DKK, ⌂ 155 DKK

An impressive 1787 former grain-drying warehouse, with an appealing maritime theme running throughout. Bedrooms feature vintage beams and bespoke wood furniture and have city or harbour views; opt for one of the duplex suites.

HERMAN K

BOUTIQUE HOTEL • TOWNHOUSE • DESIGN

Bremerholm 6 ⊠ 1069 K PLAN: C2
Ⓜ Kongens Nytorv
TEL. 33 12 42 00 – www.brochner-hotels.com
31 rm ☲ – **♦** 2100/3000 DKK **♦♦** 2500/6000 DKK
ROXIE – See restaurant listing

A design-led boutique hotel with 'industrial chic' styling in a former electricity transformer station in the heart of the city. Modern grey and white bedrooms; choose suite 507 which has its own private rooftop terrace. Relaxed service from a casually dressed team.

IMPERIAL

BUSINESS • TRADITIONAL • DESIGN

Vester Farimagsgade 9 ⊠ 1606 V PLAN: B3
Ⓜ Vesterport
TEL. 33 12 80 00 – www.imperialhotel.com
304 rm – **♦** 995/3670 DKK **♦♦** 1190/3900 DKK, ☲ 185 DKK – 1 suite

A well-known hotel, geared up for conferences and centrally located on a wide city thoroughfare. Bedrooms are particularly spacious and have a subtle Danish style. The contemporary restaurant features a brightly coloured Italian theme wall and serves Italian dishes to match.

ISLAND

BUSINESS • CHAIN • MODERN

Kalvebod Brygge 53 (via Kalvebod Brygge) ✉ 1560 V
TEL. 33 38 96 00 – www.copenhagenisland.dk
326 rm – ♦ 855/3450 DKK ♦♦ 2780/5650 DKK, ☐ 185 DKK

A contemporary glass and steel hotel set just outside the city, on a man-made island in the harbour. Bedrooms are well-equipped – some are allergy friendly and some have balconies; choose a water view over a city view. The stylish multi-level lounge-bar and restaurant serves a wide-ranging international menu.

KONG ARTHUR

TOWNHOUSE • TRADITIONAL • CLASSIC

Nørre Søgade 11 ✉ 1370 K PLAN: B2
Ⓜ Nørreport
TEL. 33 11 12 12 – www.arthurhotels.dk
155 rm – ♦ 800/3000 DKK ♦♦ 1100/3600 DKK

Four 1882 buildings set around a courtyard, in an elegant residential avenue close to Peblinge Lake. Well-equipped bedrooms have a high level of facilities. Relax in the smart Thai spa and enjoy complimentary drinks from 5-6pm.

NOBIS

HISTORIC BUILDING • LUXURY • DESIGN

Niels Brocks Gade 1 ⊠ 1574 V **PLAN: C3**
Ⓜ København Hovedbane Gård
TEL. 78 74 14 00 – www.nobishotel.dk
77 rm ⌑ – ♦ 1800/3600 DKK ♦♦ 1800/3600 DKK, – 1 suite

The impressive former music academy building sits close to Tivoli Gardens. Other than a striking staircase, little of its 20C history remains; instead it's a cool, stylish and understated space with contemporary Danish furnishings. The airy restaurant offers modern European dishes.

RADISSON COLLECTION ROYAL

BUSINESS • DESIGN

Hammerichsgade 1 ⊠ 1611 V **PLAN: B3**
Ⓜ Vesterport
TEL. 33 42 60 00 – www.radissoncollection.com/en/
royalhotel-copenhagen
261 rm – ♦ 1195/6995 DKK ♦♦ 1495/7495 DKK, ⌑ 195 DKK

A spacious hotel designed by Arne Jacobson and opened in 1960; now refreshed and updated. Bedrooms have a Scandic style – the largest are the double-aspect corner rooms; Number 606 still has its original furnishings. All-day Café Royal specialises in steaks.

SANDERS

TOWNHOUSE • ELEGANT • DESIGN

⚑ ♿ AC

Tordenskjoldsgade 15 ✉ 1055 K PLAN: D2
Ⓜ Kongens Nytorv
TEL. 46 40 00 40 – www.hotelsanders.com
54 rm ☕ – ♦ 2400/2600 DKK ♦♦ 3100/6600 DKK – 6 suites

Set in a residential area close to Nyhavn and the theatre is this neoclassical Jugendstil-style townhouse. It is intimate, homely and elegant, from the cosy open-fired living room, atmospheric cocktail bar and small all-day brasserie to the sophisticated bedrooms where no detail is overlooked. A charming young team provide friendly, attentive and personalised service.

ABSALON

FAMILY • DESIGN • ELEGANT

♿

Helgolandsgade 15 ✉ 1653 V PLAN: B3
Ⓜ København Hovedbane Gård
TEL. 33 31 43 44 – www.absalon-hotel.dk
161 rm ☕ – ♦ 1125/2160 DKK ♦♦ 1125/2160 DKK – 2 suites

A family-run hotel located close to the railway station and furnished with vibrantly coloured fabrics. Elegant, comfortable bedrooms feature an 'artbox' on the wall which celebrates an aspect of Danish design such as Lego or porcelain.

ALEXANDRA

BOUTIQUE HOTEL • BUSINESS • DESIGN

H.C. Andersens Boulevard 8 ✉ 1553 V **PLAN: B3**
Ⓜ Vesterport
TEL. 33 74 44 44 – www.hotelalexandra.dk
Closed 24-26 December
61 rm – 🛉 450/750 DKK 🛉🛉 1500/1800 DKK, ☕ 142 DKK

A well-run, late Victorian hotel in the city centre, with a contrastingly modern interior. Bedrooms are individually styled and there's an entire 'allergy friendly' floor; the 12 'Design' rooms are styled by famous Danish designers.

ANDERSEN

FAMILY • DESIGN • CONTEMPORARY

A/C

Helgolandsgade 12 ✉ 1653 V **PLAN: B3**
Ⓜ København Hovedbane Gård
TEL. 33 31 46 10 – www.andersen-hotel.dk
69 rm ☕ – 🛉 1025/2195 DKK 🛉🛉 1175/3395 DKK

Bright, funky styling marks out this boutique hotel, where the bedrooms are classified as 'Cool', 'Brilliant', 'Wonderful' and 'Amazing'. There's an honesty bar in reception and you can enjoy a complimentary glass of wine from 5–6pm.

AVENUE

BUSINESS • FAMILY • MODERN

Åboulevard 29 ✉ 1960 C **PLAN: A2**
Ⓜ Forum
TEL. 35 37 31 11 – www.brochner-hotels.dk
68 rm – ♦ 795/4000 DKK ♦♦ 1200/4000 DKK, ☕ 160 DKK

A well-maintained, family-run hotel dating back to 1899. Relax around the central bar in the smart modern lounge or out on the courtyard patio. Bedrooms have a bright, crisp style and feature striking Philippe Starck lights.

SKT. ANNÆ

BUSINESS • TOWNHOUSE • COSY

Sankt Annæ Plads 18-20 ✉ 1250 K **PLAN: D2**
Ⓜ Kongens Nytorv
TEL. 33 96 20 00 – www.hotelsanktannae.dk
145 rm – ♦ 1195/2595 DKK ♦♦ 1695/3095 DKK, ☕ 195 DKK – 1 suite

Three Victorian townhouses not far from the bustling harbourside of Nyhavn. Ask for a 'Superior' bedroom for more space and quiet; Room 601 is the best – it's accessed via the roof terrace and has its own balcony overlooking the rooftops. Italian dishes with a modern twist in the stylish restaurant.

HEBRON 🏠

TRADITIONAL • FAMILY • FUNCTIONAL

🚴

Helgolandsgade 4 ✉ 1653 V PLAN: B3
Ⓜ København Hovedbane Gård
TEL. 33 31 69 06 – www.hebron.dk
Closed 19-29 December
99 rm ☟ – 🛉 800/2045 DKK 🛉🛉 995/2245 DKK – 2 suites

A smart hotel behind a Victorian façade – this was one of the city's biggest when it opened in 1899 and some original features still remain. There's a comfy lounge and a grand breakfast room; well-kept bedrooms range in shape and size.

IBSENS 🏠

HISTORIC • FAMILY • PERSONALISED

🅿

Vendersgade 23 ✉ 1363 K PLAN: B2
Ⓜ Nørreport
TEL. 33 13 19 13 – www.arthurhotels.dk
118 rm ☟ – 🛉 750/2445 DKK 🛉🛉 1150/2820 DKK

The little sister to Kong Arthur is this simple, brightly furnished hotel with a relaxed, bohemian feel. The small bar serves breakfast, as well as complimentary drinks from 5-6pm. Bedrooms are well-kept – 'Tiny' really are compact.

PAUSTIAN ⅋○

DANISH • FASHIONABLE • DESIGN

Kalkbrænderiløbskaj 2 (North: 4 km by Folke Bernadottes Allé) ⊠ 2100 Ø
TEL. 39 18 55 01 – www.paustian.com
Closed July, 23 December-14 January and Sunday

Carte 300/570 DKK (lunch only)

A friendly, informal restaurant set in an impressive harbourside building designed by renowned architect Jørn Utzon. Traditional Danish cooking has French touches; watch the chefs at work in the open kitchen.

JORDNÆR ✿

DANISH • ROMANTIC • INTIMATE

Gentofte Hotel, Gentoftegade 29 (North : 8 km by Østbanegade and Road 2) ⊠ 2820
TEL. 22 40 80 20 – www.restaurantjordnaer.dk
Closed 3 weeks July, 1 week February, 1 week October, 22 December-2 January and Sunday-Tuesday

Menu 850/1300 DKK (dinner only) (tasting menu only)

Chef:
Eric Kragh Vildgaard

Specialities:
Turbot with green asparagus and Noilly Prat. Pike-perch with ramps and fermented garlic. Camomile, honey and green rhubarb.

The passionately run 'Down to Earth' is housed within an unassuming suburban hotel. The building dates from 1666 and the rustic modern room comes with grey painted timbers. Knowledgeably prepared dishes feature ingredients foraged by the largely self-taught chef and flavours are pure and harmonious.

DEN RØDE COTTAGE

MODERN CUISINE • COSY • RUSTIC

Strandvejen 550
(North : 12 km by Folke Bernadottes Allé and Road 2) ✉ 2930
TEL. 31 90 46 14 – www.denroedecottage.dk
Closed Sunday dinner and Monday

Menu 575/825 DKK (dinner only and Sunday lunch)
(tasting menu only) (booking essential)

Run with real enthusiasm by a young team of friends, this cosy 'Red Cottage' sits in a charming spot in a wooded park close to the sea. Dishes reflect the changing seasons and the modern, well-balanced cooking respects the classics, whilst also having its own original style.

SØLLERØD KRO ❀

MODERN CUISINE • INN • ELEGANT

Søllerødvej 35 (North : 20 km by Nørre Allé) ✉ 2840
TEL. 45 80 25 05 – www.soelleroed-kro.dk
Closed 3 weeks July, 1 week February, Easter, Sunday dinner, Monday and Tuesday

Menu 395/1195 DKK – Carte 845/1310 DKK

Specialities:
Oscietra caviar 'en surprise'. Black lobster, vin jaune and creamed morels. Gourmandise desserts.

A characterful 17C thatched inn by a pond in a picturesque village, with a delightful courtyard terrace and three elegant, intimate rooms. In keeping with the surroundings, cooking has a classical heart but is presented in a modern style. Dishes have deceptive depth and the wine list is a tome of beauty.

AARHUS
Denmark

Urilux/iStock

Known as the world's smallest big city, Denmark's second city is a vibrant, versatile place, yet has the charm of a small town. It was originally founded by the Vikings in the 8th century and has been an important trading centre ever since. It's set on the Eastern edge of Jutland and is the country's main port; lush forests surround it, and there are beautiful beaches to the north and south. It's easy to enjoy the great outdoors, while also benefiting from the advantages of urban life. There's plenty to see and do, and most of it is within walking distance: the city centre is awash with shops – from big chains to quirky boutiques – as well as museums, bars and restaurants,

and the student population contributes to its youthful feel. The most buzzing area is Aboulevarden; a pedestrianized street which runs alongside the river, lined with clubs and cafés. Cultural activities are also high on the agenda of the European Capital of Culture 2017: visit the 12th century Cathedral and the ARoS Art Museum with its colourful rooftop panorama; witness the 2000 year old Grauballe man on display at the Moesgaard prehistoric museum; or step back in time at Den Gamle By. This is not a place that stands still and bold redevelopment projects are reshaping the cityscape, with shiny new apartment and office blocks springing up around the harbour.

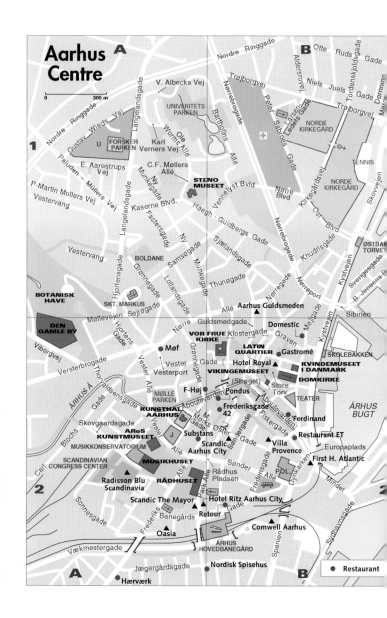

Aarhus A
Centre

0   300 m

Nordre Ringgade

V. Albecks Vej

Trøjborgvej

Otte Ruds Gade

Aldersrovej

Niels Juels Gade

Tordenskjoldsgade

Dortninn

Marts

UNIVERITETS PARKEN

Bartholins Allé

Nørrebrogade

Peter Sabroes Gade

Larsen Ledets Gade

NORDE KIRKEGÅRD

Trøjborgvej

Nordre Ringgade

Gustav Wieds Vej

Langelandsgade

Ole Allé

Worms Allé

Karl Verners Vej

FORSKER PARKEN

U

TENNIS

Paludan - Müllers Vej

E. Aarestrups Vej

C.F. Møllers Allé

STENO MUSEET

NORDE KIRKEGÅRD

Skovvejen

P-Martin Mollers Vej

Vestervang

Ny Munkegade

Kaserne Blvd.

Høegh - Guldbergs Gade

Nørre Blvd

Vennelyst Bvld

Kirkegårdsvej

Ost Blvd

Knudrisgade

ØSTBA TORVE

Vestervang

Langelandsgade

Fastersgade

BOLDANE

Gronnegade

Ny Munkegade

Samsøgade

Sjællandsgade

Nørrebrogade

Nørreport

Kystvejen

Sverigesgade

B. Jensens P

Hjortensgade

Lollandsgade

Thunøgade

Nørregade

BOTANISK HAVE

Møllevejen

Sejrøgade

Nørre Allé

Aarhus Guldsmeden

Sibirien

DEN GAMLE BY

SKT. MARKUS

Guldsmedgade

Domestic

Graven

Mejlgade

Kystvejen

Viborgvej

Hjortens Gade

VOR FRUE KIRKE

Klostergade

SKOLEBAKKEN

Vesterbrogade

Versterbrogade

Vester Gade

● Møf

LATIN QUARTIER

Gastromè ●

Thorvaldsensgade

Vester Allé

Vesterport

Hotel Royal ▲

KVINDEMUSEET I DANMARK

ÅRHUS Å

Aldersensgade

F-Høj ●

VIKINGEMUSEET

(Strøget)

Store Torv

DOMKIRKE

MØLLE PARKEN

Pondus ●

Aboulevarden

Fiskergade

TEATER

ÅRHUS BUGT

KUNSTHAL AARHUS

Skovgaardsgade

Morks Østergade

Frederiksgade ●

42 ●

Ferdinand ▲

Blochs

AROS KUNSTMUSEET

Vester Allé

J

Substans ●

Villa Provence ▲

Restaurant ET ●

MUSIKKONSERVATORIUM

Scandic Aarhus City

Sønder Allé

Europaplads

First H. Atlantic ●

Carl

SCANDINAVIAN CONGRESS CENTER

MUSIKHUSET

Park Allé

Rådhus Pladsen

Dynkarken

POL.

Mindet

Sonnesgade

Radisson Blu Scandinavia ▲

RÅDHUSET

Frederiks

Scandic The Mayor ●

Hotel Ritz Aarhus City

Frederiksgade

Sydhavnsgade

Banegårds Gade

Retour ●

Oasia ▲

ÅRHUS HOVEDBANEGÅRD

Comwell Aarhus ●

Spanien

Vækmestergade

A

Jægergårdsgade

Nordisk Spisehus ●

B

● Hærværk

● Restaurant

DOMESTIC ✿

MODERN CUISINE • FASHIONABLE • MINIMALIST   &. 🛜 ☕

Mejlgade 35B (through the arch) ✉ 8000 PLAN: B2
TEL. 6143 7010 – www.restaurantdomestic.dk
Closed 22 December-7 January, Easter, Sunday and Monday
Menu 550/950 DKK (dinner only) (tasting menu only)
(booking essential)

Chef:
Morten Rastad and Christoffer
Norton

Specialities:
Squash, oyster and yoghurt.
Pork with onion and unripe
plums. Cherries with camomile and
buttermilk.

This restaurant sets itself the challenge of only using Danish
ingredients – hence the name – so expect lots of techniques, creativity
and imagination in their 4 or 8 course menus. It's housed in a period
property that's been everything from a school to a dairy; the burnt
oak dining tables are lovely.

FREDERIKSHØJ ✿

CREATIVE • ELEGANT • LUXURY   🍸 ⪕ 🍽 AC ☕ P

Oddervej 19-21 (South: 3.5 km by Spanien
and Strandvejen) ✉ 8000
TEL. 8614 22 80 – www.frederikshoj.com
Closed 4 weeks midsummer, 1 week October, Christmas-New Year
and Sunday-Tuesday
Menu 1145 DKK (dinner only) (tasting menu only)
(booking essential)

Chef:
Wassim Hallal
Specialities:
Potatoes from Samsø. Sweetbread.
Rhubarb.

Set in the former staff lodge to the Royal Palace, this restaurant is
smart, luxurious and contemporary with edgy artwork, iPad menus
and floor to ceiling windows affording views over the gardens and out
to sea. Dishes are elaborate, creative and visually impressive. Service
is professional and knowledgeable.

CENTRE

GASTROMÉ ❀

MODERN CUISINE • FASHIONABLE • INTIMATE   ♿ 🍴

Rosensgade 28 ✉ 8000 PLAN: B2
TEL. 28 78 16 17 – www.gastrome.dk
Closed 25-26 December, Sunday and Monday
Menu 600/1100 DKK (dinner only) (tasting menu only)

Chef:
William Jørgensen
Specialities:
Lobster with cauliflower and mousseline sauce. Quail, seasonal mushrooms, burnt potato and wild herbs. 'Rødgrød': berries, white chocolate and sour cream.

This intimate Latin Quarter restaurant features a semi open plan kitchen and stark white walls punctuated with contemporary art. The menu is divided into a 'half throttle' of 4 courses and a 'full throttle' of 8, with wines to match. Complex cooking showcases modern techniques. Service is informative.

SUBSTANS ❀

MODERN CUISINE • FRIENDLY • SIMPLE   A/C

Frederiksgade 74 ✉ 8000 PLAN: A2
TEL. 86 23 04 01 – www.restaurantsubstans.dk
Closed 24-25 December and Sunday-Tuesday
Menu 800/1200 DKK (dinner only) (tasting menu only)

Chef:
René Mammen
Specialities:
Scallop with tomatoes, camomile and pine. Pork with pumpkin, squash and coriander. Rhubarb, lilac, cream and hazel.

Classically Scandic in style, with a fresh, uncluttered feel, Pondus' older, more adventurous sister is run by the same experienced husband and wife team. Creative, contemporary cooking uses top quality, mostly organic, ingredients. Dishes have original touches, distinct flavours and stimulating combinations.

HÆRVÆRK 🍴

DANISH • INTIMATE • RUSTIC

 ♿ A/C

Frederiks Allé 105 ✉ 8000 PLAN: A2
TEL. 50 51 26 51 – www.restaurant-haervaerk.dk
Closed Sunday-Tuesday
Menu 455 DKK (dinner only) (tasting menu only)

Run with plenty of passion and enthusiasm by a group of friends. The place has an ersatz industrial feel, thanks to the concrete floor, stark white décor and a glass-fronted fridge of hanging meats. The menu focuses on organic Danish produce in dishes that are earthy, natural and satisfying.

PONDUS 🍴

DANISH • BISTRO • RUSTIC

Åboulevarden 51 ✉ 8000 PLAN: B2
TEL. 28 77 18 50 – www.restaurantpondus.dk
Closed 24-25 December
Menu 325 DKK – Carte 375/405 DKK (dinner only)

Set by the narrow city centre canal, the little sister to Substans is a small, rustic bistro with a friendly vibe and a stripped-back style. The blackboard menu offers flavoursome cooking which uses organic Danish produce. Dishes are bright and colourful and represent great value.

F-HØJ ‖◎

SMØRREBRØD • NEIGHBOURHOOD • FRIENDLY

Grønnegade 2 ✉ 8000 **PLAN: A2**
www.fhoj.dk
Closed 4 weeks midsummer, 1 week October, Christmas-New Year,
and Sunday-Tuesday
Carte 235/245 DKK (lunch only) (bookings not accepted)

A bright, busy café with a pavement terrace; fridges and cabinets
display a tempting selection of desserts, cakes, biscuits and drinks.
There are three hot and six cold dishes on the smørrebrød menu; two
plus dessert should suffice.

FERDINAND ‖◎

FRENCH • BRASSERIE • COSY   88 ⌂ AC

Åboulevarden 28 ✉ 8000 **PLAN: B2**
TEL. 87 32 14 44 – www.hotelferdinand.dk
Closed 22 December-5 January
Menu 445 DKK (dinner) – Carte 345/435 DKK

Red-canopied Ferdinand stands out from its neighbours on the
liveliest street in the city. From the open kitchen come dishes that
mix French and Danish influences; the rib-eye is a constant. Bedrooms
are comfy and spacious and there are apartments with small balconies
for longer stays.

FREDERIKSGADE 42 🍴

DANISH • NEIGHBOURHOOD • BISTRO

Frederiksgade 42 ✉ 8000 **PLAN: B2**
TEL. 60 68 96 06 - www.frederiksgade42.dk
Closed 23 December-4 January, Sunday and Monday
Menu 368 DKK - Carte 324/344 DKK (dinner only)

The larger-than-life owner extends a warm welcome to customers at this delightful restaurant in the heart of the city. The seasonal menu is geared 80:20 in favour of vegetables against meat/fish; the well-priced plates are designed for sharing.

GHRELIN 🍴

MODERN CUISINE • CHIC • NEIGHBOURHOOD

Bernhardt Jensens Boulevard 125 (Northeast: 2.5 km by Kystvejen) ✉ 8000
TEL. 30 13 30 04 - www.ghrelin.dk
Closed 24-25 December and Sunday-Wednesday
Menu 650/1250 DKK (dinner only) (tasting menu only) (booking essential)

A sleek, modern two-roomed restaurant with a semi-open kitchen and confident friendly service in the heart of the up-and-coming dockland area. 3, 5 or 7 course tasting menus with the occasional surprise thrown in; good quality produce is used to create well-presented dishes.

MEJERIET ⅋O

MODERN CUISINE • DESIGN • RUSTIC   🐜 🛏 ✷ **P**

Vilhelmsborg, Bedervej 101, Mårslet (South: 11 km by 451) ✉ 8320
TEL. 86 93 71 95 – www.restaurant-mejeriet.dk
Closed 23 December-3 January, 11 July-5 August, Monday-
Wednesday and Sunday dinner
Menu 525 DKK – Carte 365/495 DKK (dinner only and Sunday
lunch) (booking essential)

Converted stables next to a 19C manor house host this enthusiastically
run, characterful restaurant. The cooking is a little less elaborate than
in previous years but just as enjoyable, with a set menu alongside an
à la carte. Some of the ingredients are supplied by the owner himself,
a keen hunter.

MØF ⅋O

DANISH • NEIGHBOURHOOD • TRENDY

Vesterport 10 ✉ 8000 **PLAN: A2**
TEL. 61 73 33 33 – www.restaurantmoef.com
Closed 24-26 December, 1-2 January, Tuesday and Wednesday
Menu 349 DKK – Carte 397/517 DKK (dinner only)
(booking essential)

Ask for a seat at the counter to watch the young chef-owners cook
in the open kitchen. The three different menus presented at dinner
allow for some flexibility; dishes are Danish at heart and made with
local produce.

NORDISK SPISEHUS 🍴

MODERN CUISINE • NEIGHBOURHOOD • FASHIONABLE

M.P.Bruuns Gade 31 ✉ 8000 **PLAN: A/B2**
TEL. 86 17 70 99 – www.nordiskspisehus.dk
Closed 24-26 December, 1 January and Sunday

Menu 267/699 DKK

An intimate restaurant with attentive, professional service, set just behind the main station. Flavourful modern Danish dishes, often inspired by successful chefs around the globe. Wine pairings accompany the 3,5 and 7 course evening tasting menus.

RESTAURANT ET 🍴

FRENCH • DESIGN • FASHIONABLE

Åboulevarden 7 ✉ 8000 **PLAN: B2**
TEL. 86 13 88 00 – www.restaurant-et.dk
Closed 23 December-7 January and Sunday

Menu 369 DKK – Carte 246/497 DKK

A bright, contemporary and smoothly run brasserie split between a number of floors, including the cellar which doubles as the private dining room. The familiar Gallic dishes are generous in size and robust in flavour and come accompanied by an extensive, exclusively French wine list.

RETOUR

MEATS AND GRILLS • FASHIONABLE • BISTRO

Banegårdspladsen 4 ⊠ 8000 **PLAN: B2**
TEL. 88 63 02 90 – www.retouraarhus.dk
Closed 24-25 December and 1 January

Carte 240/595 DKK (dinner only)

A busy restaurant close to station, now offering greater choice and not quite as steak-based as it was when it first opened, although, the Danish rib-eye with fluffy homemade chips is still a feature. The midweek set menu is a steal.

COMWELL AARHUS

BUSINESS • MODERN • DESIGN

Værkmestergade 2 ⊠ 8000 **PLAN: B2**
TEL. 86 72 80 00 – www.comwellaarhus.dk
240 rm ⌷ – ♦ 1100/2000 DKK ♦♦ 1300/2200 DKK

A stylish, modern hotel set over 12 floors of a tower block. With 19 meeting rooms, it's aimed at businesspeople; the largest has space for 475. Bedrooms are bright and contemporary with monsoon showers; choose a corner Business Class room for super city views. Guest areas include a bar and buzzy bistro.

RADISSON BLU SCANDINAVIA

BUSINESS • CHAIN • MODERN

Margrethepladsen 1 ✉ 8000 **PLAN: A2**
TEL. 86 12 86 65 – www.radissonblu.com/en/hotel-aarhus
234 rm – ♦ 895/1955 DKK ♦♦ 995/2095 DKK – 5 suites

A conference-orientated hotel close to the ARoS Museum. Spacious, contemporary bedrooms offer all the facilities a modern traveller would expect. Business Class rooms and suites on the top two floors offer the best views along with extra touches. Open plan Nordic Brasserie and Bar.

SCANDIC AARHUS CITY

BUSINESS • CHAIN • MODERN

Østergade 10 ✉ 8000 **PLAN: B2**
TEL. 89 31 81 00 – www.scandichotels.com/aarhus
228 rm ⊊ – ♦ 700/2600 DKK ♦♦ 800/2800 DKK – 8 suites

Behind the 19C façade of a Viennese Renaissance café lies a smart, modern hotel with an open-plan lobby, lounge and bar. Bright bedrooms display photos of city scenes and the suites come with balconies. Solar panels supply electricity and rooftop hives provide honey. Smart cellar restaurant with an open kitchen.

VILLA PROVENCE

TOWNHOUSE • TRADITIONAL • PERSONALISED

🔥 **P**

Fredens Torv 10-12 ✉ 8000 **PLAN: B2**
TEL. 86 18 24 00 – www.villaprovence.dk
Closed 20 December-2 January

39 rm ☕ – 👤 1295/1895 DKK 👫 1395/3300 DKK

This charming townhouse is proudly run by an amiable couple and brings a little bit of Provence to Aarhus. Enter through the archway into a lovely cobbled garden designed by Tage Anderson, then head inside to be surrounded by books and French antiques. Bedrooms are individually styled; some have four-posters.

FIRST H. ATLANTIC

BUSINESS • CHAIN • MODERN

◁ ✿ ♿ **P**

Europaplads 10 ✉ 8000 **PLAN: B2**
TEL. 86 13 11 11 – www.firsthotels.dk

102 rm ☕ – 👤 995/1895 DKK 👫 1095/2195 DKK

Although its exterior can hardly be deemed charming, its rooms are spacious and modern with good facilities, a balcony and a vista of either the city or the sea. Enjoy breakfast with a view on the top floor. Classic Italian dishes are served in the smart restaurant. Gym membership is available at the adjacent fitness club.

HOTEL RITZ AARHUS CITY

HISTORIC • TRADITIONAL • ART DÉCO

Banegårdspladsen 12 ⊠ 8000 **PLAN: A2**

TEL. 86 13 44 44 – www.hotelritz.dk
Closed 24-25 December
67 rm ☕ – 🛉 875/1095 DKK 🛉🛉 1095/1195 DKK

An iconic 1932 hotel in distinctive yellow brick, situated across the road from the railway station. It's friendly and welcoming with an appealing art deco style and neat, modern bedrooms in warm colours; most rooms have a shower only.

HOTEL ROYAL

HISTORIC • TRADITIONAL • CLASSIC

🎏 ⅃ⅆ 🄰🄲 🖽

Store Torv 4 ⊠ 8000 **PLAN: B2**
TEL. 86 12 00 11 – www.hotelroyal.dk
63 rm – 🛉 995/1895 DKK 🛉🛉 1195/2095 DKK, ☕ 95 DKK – 5 suites

Beside the cathedral is the city's oldest hotel; 2019 marks its 181st birthday and it has a wonderfully classical feel – enhanced by paintings depicting Denmark's Kings and Queens. Very spacious bedrooms combine antique furniture and modern facilities.

SCANDIC THE MAYOR

BUSINESS • MODERN • DESIGN

Banegårdspladsen 14 ✉ 8000 PLAN: A2
TEL. 87 32 01 00 – www.scandichotels.dk/themayor
162 rm ☕ – 👤 695/2095 DKK 👫 895/2595 DKK

A well run and good value corporate hotel situated close to the railway station. The cosy, contemporary bedrooms have an industrial feel; those to the rear of the building are quieter. The spacious and relaxed Italian restaurant serves a seasonal modern menu.

AARHUS GULDSMEDEN

TOWNHOUSE • TRADITIONAL • PERSONALISED

Guldsmedgade 40 ✉ 8000 PLAN: B1
TEL. 86 13 45 50 – www.guldsmedenhotels.com
22 rm ☕ – 👤 945/1345 DKK 👫 1075/1475 DKK

A relaxed hotel with an eco/organic ethos and a friendly atmosphere. Simply decorated bedrooms vary in shape and size; some feature antique furniture and the larger ones have four-posters. They offer complimentary tea, coffee and juice.

OASIS

TOWNHOUSE • TRADITIONAL • DESIGN

Kriegersvej 27-31 ⊠ 8000 PLAN: A2
TEL. 87 32 37 15 – www.hoteloasia.com
Closed 23-26 December

65 rm ☕ – 🕴 895/1095 DKK 🕴🕴 1095/1295 DKK

After a day's sightseeing or shopping, you will be happy to head back
to this well-kept hotel in a quieter area of the city. Bright, uncluttered
bedrooms offer good facilities; go for one of the design rooms or the
four-poster.

TABU 🍴

REGIONAL CUISINE • FRIENDLY • TRADITIONAL DÉCOR [A/C]

Vesterå 5 ⊠ 9000
TEL. 88 19 60 58 – www.ta-bu.dk
Closed July, 24-27 December, 1 January and Sunday-Tuesday

Menu 400/950 DKK (dinner only)

The enthusiastic team provide a gastronomic tour of North Jutland:
all the produce comes from this region and dishes are named after the
area from which their main ingredient is sourced. Carefully cooked
modern dishes offer distinct textures and flavours; most come in
two servings.

KADEAU BORNHOLM ✿

CREATIVE • MINIMALIST • SIMPLE   ← 🏠 **P**

Baunevej 18, Vestre Sømark Pedersker, Åkirkeby (Southeast : 23 km by 38) ✉ 3720
TEL. 56 97 82 50 – www.kadeau.dk
Closed 30 September-29 April and Monday-Wednesday in low season

Menu 1300 DKK (dinner only) (tasting menu only)
(booking essential)

Chef:
Nicolai Nørregaard

Specialities:
Baltic prawn toast with dried ceps & cockle emulsion. Potatoes, blueberry, lovage and fig leaf oil. Caramelised buttermilk tart, fir cones and spruce.

A remote beachside eatery with a superb sea panorama; this is best enjoyed from the terrace, although all tables have a view. The atmosphere is relaxed but they are serious about food here, with a tasting menu offering accomplished, original cooking with superbly balanced, contrasting flavours.

STAMMERSHALLE BADEHOTEL 🍴

MODERN CUISINE • CONTEMPORARY DÉCOR   🕸 ← 🚲 **P**

Sdr. Strandvej 128, Stammershalle, Gudhjem (Northeast : 24 km by 159 on 158) ✉ 3760
TEL. 56 48 42 10 – www.stammershalle-badehotel.dk
Closed mid December-February and Tuesday-Wednesday March, April and October
Menu 595 DKK (dinner) – Carte 265/650 DKK (booking essential)

A light and airy New England style restaurant in a charming coastal hotel, offering stunning sea views. Seasonal island ingredients are prepared with skill and passion by the young kitchen and the modern dishes have distinct flavours and interesting combinations. In summer they open at lunch for smørrebrød.

STAMMERSHALLE BADEHOTEL

LUXURY • SEASIDE

< ♨ ☆ ✗ ⌁ 🦢 **P**

Sdr. Strandvej 128, Stammershalle, Gudhjem
(Northeast : 24 km by 159 on 158) ✉ 3760
TEL. 56 48 42 10 – www.stammershalle-badehotel.dk
Closed 1 November-28 February
15 rm ⌂ – 🛉 950 DKK 🛉🛉 1200/1550 DKK

STAMMERSHALLE BADEHOTEL – See restaurant listing

This cosy hotel opened in 1911 and is run with passion. Stylish whilst also respecting tradition, it is situated in an enviable position and boasts superb sea views – you can even go bathing in the Baltic just across the road. Bedrooms have straightforward comforts and a simple Scandinavian style.

MOLSKROEN 🍴

MODERN CUISINE • CONTEMPORARY DÉCOR •
DESIGN   < ♨ 🏠 ⌂ **P**

Molskroen Hotel • Hovedgaden 16, Femmøller Strand (Northwest : 7 km by 21) ✉ 8400
TEL. 86 36 22 00 – www.molskroen.dk
Closed January, 16-30 December, Sunday-Wednesday February-March and lunch September-May

Carte 600/1950 DKK (booking essential)

A stylish, relaxed and well-regarded seaside inn with a reputation for gastronomy; a table on the charming terrace is the perfect spot to enjoy traditional French cuisine as well as more modern interpretations of the classics.

MOLSKROEN

INN • LUXURY • CONTEMPORARY

Hovedgaden 16, Femmøller Strand (Northwest : 7 km by 21) ⊠ 8400
TEL. 86 36 22 00 – www.molskroen.dk
Closed January, 16-30 December and Sunday-Wednesday
February-March

8 rm – ♦ 950/1600 DKK ♦♦ 1280/1680 DKK – 10 suites ⌓ –
♦ 2100/3500 DKK ♦♦ 2100/3500 DKK

MOLSKROEN – See restaurant listing

This inn, located in Mols Bjerge National Park, was built by renowned
architect Egil Fischer in 1923 and over the years it has gained a
considerable reputation. The traditional timbered façade contrasts
with its stylish, modern interior.

KOKS ❀❀

CREATIVE • CONTEMPORARY DÉCOR • INTIMATE

Frammi við Gjónna, Leynavatn (Northeast: 2.75 km by 51, 40 and
unmade gravel track beside lake Leynavatn) ⊠ 335
TEL. 333 999 – www.koks.fo
Closed December-February, Sunday and Monday

Menu 1400 DKK (dinner only) (tasting menu only)
(booking essential)

Specialities:
Tartare of halibut with watercress.
Razorbill and beetroot. Dulse with
blueberry.

Meet at the lakeside fermenting hut for an aperitif with a view; you
will then be delivered to the picturesque former farmhouse and forge
for an intimate dining experience. The creative 17-19 course menu
champions the finest Faroese produce with an emphasis on traditional
techniques. Seafood is a highlight.

TI TRIN NED ⚜

MODERN CUISINE • FRIENDLY • NEIGHBOURHOOD 🅰🅺 ⬦ 🅿

Toldkammeret 9 ✉ 7000
TEL. 75 93 33 55 – www.titrinned.dk
Closed 3 weeks July-August, Christmas and Sunday-Tuesday
Menu 875/1200 DKK (dinner only) (tasting menu only)
(booking essential)

Chef:
Rainer Gassner

Specialities:
Scallop with green pear, salted
cucumber and dill juice. Fillet
of veal with garden vegetables.
Ice cream with birch syrup and
aromatic herbs.

New premises in 2019 for this experienced couple, after 17 years in
their basement restaurant. The two set menus are guided by produce
from their own farm. Dishes are original yet understated, mix the
classic and the modern and provide real depth of flavour.

HENNE KIRKEBY KRO ⚜⚜

CLASSIC CUISINE • INN • FRIENDLY ⚜ 🛋 ♿ 🅿

Strandvejen 234 (on 465) ✉ 6854
TEL. 75 25 54 00 – www.hennekirkebykro.dk
Closed 16 December-14 March, Wednesday dinner March-
April and Sunday-Wednesday lunch
Menu 695/1295 DKK (tasting menu only) (booking essential)

Chef:
Paul Cunningham

Specialities:
Buttered caviar crumpet. Whole
roasted turbot with garden leeks.
'Dame Nellie Melba'.

A charming 18C thatched inn with a contrastingly modern interior.
Top-notch seasonal produce celebrates their kitchen garden and the
surrounding farmland. Cooking is founded on the classics and dishes
are original and technically accomplished – the sauces are sublime.
Service is attentive and very personable. Luxurious, super-stylish
bedrooms complete the picture.

BRYGHUSET VENDIA - GOURMET 🍴

CREATIVE • INTIMATE • CONTEMPORARY DÉCOR [A/C] [P]

Markedsgade 9 ⊠ 9800
TEL. 98 92 22 29 – www.bryghusetvendia.dk
Closed July, 24-26 December and Sunday-Wednesday
Menu 2000 DKK (dinner only) (surprise menu only) (booking essential)

A microbrewery with a stylish brasserie and a tiny gourmet restaurant. The latter consists of just three tables and serves an 11 course themed surprise menu of creative, elaborately presented dishes, designed to stimulate the taste buds.

SLOTSKØKKENET ✿

CREATIVE • INTIMATE • FRIENDLY 🦐 🍷 [P]

Dragsholm Slot Hotel • Dragsholm Allé (Northwest : 6.5 km by 231 on 225) ⊠ 4534
TEL. 59 65 33 00 – www.dragsholm-slot.dk
Closed 23-24 December, Tuesday-Wednesday in winter and Sunday-Monday
Menu 1000/1200 DKK (dinner only) (tasting menu only) (booking essential)

Specialities:
Glazed carrots with pickled hemp and smoked bacon. Today's harvest with cod tongue and mussels. Bog oak, parsnip, chocolate and black cherry.

Expect to be taken on a gastronomic journey thanks to around 20 servings of carefully crafted, innovative and intensely flavoured dishes created using local, foraged, seasonal or preserved produce. This atmospheric cellar restaurant is set in the former kitchens of an impressive 800 year old castle.

DRAGSHOLM SLOT

HISTORIC BUILDING • FAMILY • GRAND LUXURY

⟨ 🐿 🛏 🏠 🛁 **P**

Dragsholm Allé (Northwest : 6.5 km by 231 on 225) ✉ 4534
TEL. 59 65 33 00 – www.dragsholm-slot.dk
Closed 23-24 December
41 rm ⌷ – 🚹 2000 DKK 🚻 2300 DKK
SLOTSKØKKENET ❀ – See restaurant listing

A charming 800 year old fortified manor house with beautiful grounds
and a moat; one of the oldest secular buildings in Denmark. The
interior is modern yet full of character, with luxurious, classically
decorated bedrooms featuring antique furniture and four-poster
beds. Dine in the relaxed bistro, Spisehuset, or enjoy a gastronomic
experience in Slotskøkkenet.

SLETTEN 🍴○

MODERN CUISINE • DESIGN • FASHIONABLE &⟨ 🏮 ⇄

Gl Strandvej 137 ✉ 3050
TEL. 49 19 13 21 – www.sletten.dk
Closed 24 December-9 January, Sunday and Monday October-April
Menu 450/600 DKK – Carte 405/825 DKK (booking essential)

A relaxed former inn in a charming coastal village; most people head
to the room with the sea view, although the others with their bold
foodie pictures are equally as pleasant. Well-presented modern small
plates make up the menu – 2-3 per person is about right. The wine list
provides plenty of interest.

FALSLED KRO 🍴

CLASSIC CUISINE • ELEGANT • COUNTRY HOUSE   🅿

Falsled Kro Hotel • Assensvej 513 ✉ 5642
TEL. 62 68 11 11 – www.falsledkro.dk
Closed 15-27 December, 1-15 January, Monday in winter, Tuesday
January-February, lunch September-May and Sunday

Menu 875/1795 DKK (dinner) – Carte lunch 455/625 DKK (bookings
essential for non-residents)

A formal hotel dining room with rustic beams, a vast feature fireplace,
an open kitchen and an extension overlooking the garden. Set 4, 6 or 8
course menus offer accomplished, classically based dishes with bold
flavours and modern touches. Ingredients are top-notch and service
is detailed and professional.

FALSLED KRO   🏠

INN • HISTORIC • ELEGANT

🛏 🍸 ♿ 🅿

Assensvej 513 ✉ 5642
TEL. 62 68 11 11 – www.falsledkro.dk
Closed 15-27 December and 1-15 January

19 rm – 🚹 1675/2175 DKK 🚻 2475/2975 DKK, 🍽 285 DKK – 9 suites
FALSLED KRO – See restaurant listing

In a small village off the beaten track you will find this professionally
run, historic inn with a hugely characterful interior boasting flagged
floors, wooden beams and a pretty central courtyard. Some bedrooms
are in the original building; others are in the charming period cottages
across the road.

PASFALL ⫶○

MODERN CUISINE • FASHIONABLE • DESIGN [A/C]

Brandts Passage 31 ⊠ 5000
TEL. 23 27 00 00 – www.pasfall.dk
Closed 15 July-1 August, 22 December-8 January, Sunday and
Monday
Menu 395/1195 DKK – Carte 705/815 DKK

Watch the eponymous chef at work in the open kitchen of this bright,
contemporary restaurant. Top seasonal ingredients are used to create
robustly flavoured dishes which are classic in their foundation but
modern in delivery.

VÅR ⫶○

MODERN CUISINE • FASHIONABLE • FRIENDLY

Vintapperstræde 10 ⊠ 5000
TEL. 26 49 26 44 – www.vaar.dk
Closed Christmas-New Year and Sunday-Tuesday
Menu 550/850 DKK (dinner only) (tasting menu only)
(booking essential)

A friendly restaurant with only six tables, set on a historic cobbled
street. The simple dish descriptions on the 5 and 10 course menus
belie the complexity of the creative, flavoursome cooking. Interesting
wine recommendations focus on biodynamic and organic choices.

FREDERIKSMINDE ✿

CREATIVE • ELEGANT • INTIMATE

Hotel Frederiksminde • Klosternakken 9 ✉ 4720
TEL. 55 90 90 30 – www.frederiksminde.com
Closed 1-14 January, 23-27 December, Sunday-Monday and lunch
Tuesday-Thursday September-May
Menu 550/1395 DKK (tasting menu only) (booking essential)

Chef:
Jonas Mikkelsen

Specialities:
Flounder with cabbage, mussel
and thyme sauce. Lamb, summer
pickles and ramsons. Ice cream
with berries, plums and fermented
honey.

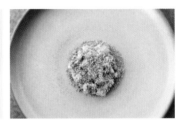

A spacious and airy hotel summer room with an aspect that takes
in the garden and the fjord. Creative modern cooking uses superb
seasonal ingredients in original yet well-judged combinations.
Dishes are precisely crafted and attractively presented and service
is knowledgeable and professional.

FREDERIKSMINDE

COUNTRY HOUSE • HISTORIC BUILDING • ELEGANT

Klosternakken 8 ✉ 4720
TEL. 55 90 90 30 – www.frederiksminde.com
Closed 1-14 January
19 rm 🛏 – 🛏 1145 DKK 🛏 2045 DKK
FREDERIKSMINDE ✿ – See restaurant listing

An attractive 19C house named after a former king of Denmark; it has
a classic, understated style and offers superb views. Bedrooms are
tastefully furnished, well-kept and comfortable; antiques and fine
portraits feature.

MOMENT 🍃
MODERN CUISINE • RUSTIC • DESIGN

Ravnen 1 (Southeast : 8 km. by Grenåvej off Ebeltoftvej/Route 21) ✉ 8410
TEL. 51 36 26 56 – www.restaurantmoment.dk
Closed 24-26 and 31 December, 1-4 January, Sunday in winter and Monday-Tuesday

Menu 350/475 DKK (dinner only and Saturday lunch)
(booking essential)

An ecologically friendly restaurant in the hamlet of Friland; the focus is on sustainability so furniture is locally made from natural wood and produce comes from its own permaculture garden or from local suppliers. The well-priced vegetable and plant based dishes are full of flavour.

RUTHS GOURMET RESTAURANT ⬥
MODERN CUISINE • DESIGN • FASHIONABLE

Ruths Hotel • Hans Ruth Vej 1 (West : 5 km. by 40) ✉ 9990
TEL. 98 44 11 24 – www.ruths-hotel.dk
Closed 2-16 January, Tuesday-Thursday October-February and Tuesday-Wednesday March, Sunday and Monday

Menu 895 DKK (dinner only) (tasting menu only)
(booking essential)

Your meal starts with a personal introduction from the chef at this seaside hotel in Denmark's most northerly town. Set menus offer creative, elaborate modern cooking. Opening times change throughout the year.

RUTHS

TRADITIONAL • FAMILY • CONTEMPORARY

🏡 🖼 🛖 🏊 P

Hans Ruth Vej 1 (West : 5 km. by 40) ✉ 9990
TEL. 98 44 11 24 – www.ruths-hotel.dk
Closed 2-16 January

52 rm ☕ – 👤 2100/2400 DKK 👫 2100/2400 DKK – 5 suites
RUTHS GOURMET RESTAURANT – See restaurant listing

A long-standing seaside hotel, where families are made to feel particularly welcome. Bedrooms are spread over a number of adjoining properties and are bright, comfortable and up-to-date. Enjoy creative, modern cooking in Ruths Gourmet Restaurant or bistro classics in the relaxed French Brasserie.

THE RESTAURANT BY KROUN 🍴

MODERN CUISINE • DESIGN • INTIMATE ≼ 🛏 ♿ A/C 🍽 P

Kurhotel Skodsborg • Skodsborg Strandvej 139 ✉ 2942
TEL. 27 90 28 64 – www.skodsborg.dk
Closed Christmas, Easter, July and Sunday-Wednesday

Menu 700/900 DKK (dinner only)
(booking essential)

A stylish, formal restaurant on the ground floor of a grand Victorian spa hotel; each of the seven tables has a view across the water. Tasting menus feature creative, elaborate, modern dishes. The chef's table is popular.

KURHOTEL SKODSBORG

LUXURY • SPA AND WELLNESS • CONTEMPORARY

⟨ 🛋 ⚲ ♿ 🖼 ⑩ 🛁 ⚒ ⚙ **P**

Skodsborg Strandvej 139 ✉ 2942
TEL. 45 58 58 00 – www.skodsborg.dk
83 rm ☕ – 👤 1400/2300 DKK 👥 1700/2600 DKK – 2 suites
THE RESTAURANT BY KROUN – See restaurant listing

A grand hotel with a world-renowned spa; founded in 1898 and
rejuvenated by a substantial facelift. Luxury bedrooms have a modern
style; choose one with a balcony to make the most of the view across
the Øresund Strait. Enjoy a cocktail on the rooftop terrace or a relaxed
meal in the brasserie.

ME|MU ✿

MODERN CUISINE • INTIMATE • HISTORIC

Torvegade 9D ✉ 7100
TEL. 21 14 00 77 – www.memu-gourmet.dk
Closed 3 weeks July, Christmas, New Year, Easter and Sunday-
Tuesday
Menu 800/1000 DKK (dinner only) (tasting menu only)
(booking essential)

Chef:
Michael Munk

Specialities:
Langoustines, raspberry,
redcurrant and horseradish. Beef
tenderloin, onions, garlic and
cherry. Blackcurrants, hay ice
cream and rye bread porridge.

This brightly decorated cellar on a pedestrianised shopping street
provides a stylish backdrop for some sophisticated cooking. Well-
judged, intensely flavoured dishes respect Danish tradition but have
a subtle modernity; choose 12 or 17 courses. Ingredients are top-notch
and the wine list is outstanding.

alekseystemmer/iStock

FINLAND

STARS & BIB GOURMAND

HELSINKI

Finland

J. Arnold Images/hemis.fr

Cool, clean and chic, the 'Daughter of the Baltic' sits prettily on a peninsula, jutting out between the landmasses of its historical overlords, Sweden and Russia. Surrounded on three sides by water, Helsinki is a busy port, but that only tells a small part of the story: forests grow in abundance around here and trees reach down to the lapping shores. This is a striking city to look at: it was rebuilt in the 19C after a fire, and many of the buildings have a handsome neoclassical or art nouveau façade. Shoppers can browse the picturesque

outdoor food and tourist markets stretching along the main harbour, where island-hopping ferries ply their trade. In a country with over 200,000 lakes it would be pretty hard to escape a green sensibility, and the Finnish capital has made sure that concrete and stone have never taken priority over its distinctive features of trees, water and open space. There are bridges at every turn connecting the city's varied array of small islands, and a ten kilometre strip of parkland acts as a spine running vertically up from the centre. Renowned as a city of cool, it's somewhere that also revels in a hot nightlife and even hotter saunas – this is where they were invented. And if your blast of dry heat has left you wanting a refreshing dip, there's always a freezing lake close at hand.

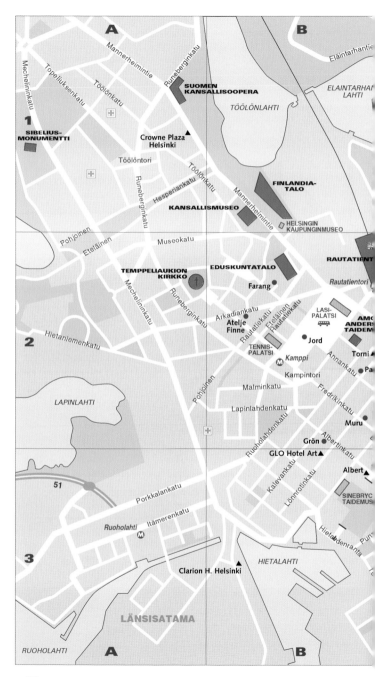

A

B

Mechelininkatu

Mannerheimintie

Topeliuksenkatu

Töölönkatu

Runeberginkatu

Eläintarhantie

SUOMEN KANSALLISOOPERA

ELÄINTARHAN LAHTI

TÖÖLÖNLAHTI

1

SIBELIUS-MONUMENTTI

Crowne Plaza Helsinki ▲

Töölöntori

Runeberginkatu

Hesperiankatu

Töölönkatu

Mannerheimintie

FINLANDIA-TALO

KANSALLISMUSEO

HELSINGIN KAUPUNGINMUSEO

Pohjoinen

Eteläinen

Museokatu

RAUTATIE

TEMPPELIAUKION KIRKKO

EDUSKUNTATALO

Mechelininkatu

Runeberginkatu

Farang ●

Rautatientori

Arkadiankatu

Atelje Finne ●

Rautatiekatu

Eteläinen Rautatiekatu

LASI-PALATSI

AMO ANDERS TAIDEM

Hietaniemenkatu

2

TENNIS-PALATSI

Jord ●

Annankatu

Torni ▲

Ⓜ Kamppi

Pa ●

Kampintori

Malminkatu

Lapinlahdenkatu

Pohjoinen

Fredrikinkatu

Muru ●

LAPINLAHTI

Ruoholahdenkatu

Grön ●

Albertinkatu

GLO Hotel Art ▲

Albert ▲

51

Porkkalankatu

Kalevankatu

Lönnrotinkatu

SINEBRYC TAIDEMUS

Itämerenkatu

Ruoholahti Ⓜ

Hietalahdenranta

Pun

3

HIETALAHTI

Clarion H. Helsinki ▲

LÄNSISATAMA

RUOHOLAHTI

A

B

92

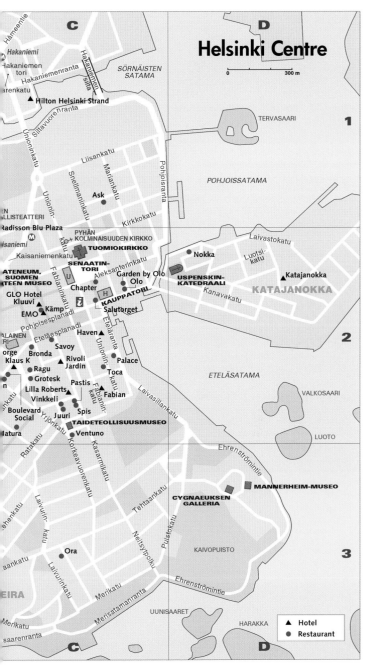

Helsinki Centre

Hakaniemi
Hakaniemen tori
arenkatu

Hämeentie

C

D

SÖRNÄISTEN SATAMA

0   300 m

TERVASAARI

1

▲ Hilton Helsinki Strand

Siltavuorenranta

Unioninkatu

Liisankatu

Snellmaninkatu

Mariankatu

POHJOISSATAMA

Pohjoisranta

Ask ●

Kirkkokatu

Unionin-

EN
ALLISTEATTERI

Radisson Blu Plaza Ⓜ

isaniemi

Kaisaniemenkatu

PYHÄN
KOLMINAISUUDEN KIRKKO

TUOMIOKIRKKO

Laivastokatu

Luotsi-katu

Nokka ●

SENAATIN-TORI

ATENEUM,
SUOMEN
TEEN MUSEO

Aleksanterinkatu

Garden by Olo
Olo ●

USPENSKIN-KATEDRAALI

▲ Katajanokka

KATAJANOKKA

GLO Hotel
Kluuvi ▲

Chapter ●

Fabianinkatu

KAUPPATORI

H

Kanavakatu

EMO ● Kämp ▲

Pohjoisesplanadi

i

Salutorget ●

ALAINEN
RI

Eteläesplanadi

Haven ▲

Etelaranta

orge
Klaus K ▲

Bronda ●

Savoy ●

Rivoli ●
Jardin ▲

Unionin-katu

Palace ●

Toca ●

ETELÄSATAMA

VALKOSAARI

n

Ragu ●

Grotesk ●

Pastis ●

Fabianinkatu

Fabian ●

Laivasillankatu

Lilla Roberts ▲
Vinkkeli ●

LUOTO

katu

Boulevard
Social ●

Juuri ●

Spis ●

TAIDETEOLLISUUSMUSEO

Yrjönkatu

Ehrenströmintie

Natura ●

Ventuno ●

Korkeavuorenkatu

Kasarmikatu

Ratakatu

MANNERHEIM-MUSEO

Laivurin-katu

CYGNAEUKSEN
GALLERIA

Tehtaankatu

Puistokatu

ehenkatu

Laivurin-katu

Ora ●

Laivurinkatu

KAIVOPUISTO

3

aankatu

Neitsytpolku

EIRA

Merikatu

Ehrenströmintie

Merikatu

Merisatamanranta

UUNISAARET

saarenranta

C

HARAKKA

D

▲ Hotel
● Restaurant

ASK ✿

MODERN CUISINE • INTIMATE • COSY

`A/C`

Vironkatu 8 ✉ 00170 **PLAN: C1**
Ⓜ Kaisaniemi
TEL. 040 5818100 – www.restaurantask.fi
Closed Easter, Christmas, Sunday-Tuesday and bank holidays

Menu 65/119€ (dinner only and lunch Friday-Saturday)
(tasting menu only)

Chef:
Filip Langhoff

Specialities:
Smoked reindeer tartare and hazelnut. Pike-perch with Finnish caviar and nasturtium. Pancakes with spruce shoots and brown butter ice cream.

It may be hidden away but this welcoming restaurant is well-known. It's a charming place, run by a delightful, experienced couple, who offer modern Nordic cooking crafted almost entirely from organic ingredients. Dishes are light and original, produce is top quality and flavours are clearly defined.

DEMO ✿

MODERN CUISINE • INTIMATE • ROMANTIC

Uudenmaankatu 9-11 ✉ 00120 **PLAN: C2**
Ⓜ Rautatientori
TEL. 09 22890840 – www.restaurantdemo.fi
Closed 2 weeks July-August, 2 weeks Christmas, Easter, midsummer, Sunday and Monday

Menu 65/105€ (dinner only) (tasting menu only)
(booking essential)

Chef:
Tommi Tuominen

Specialities:
Duck liver mousse, truffle cream. Beef with sweetbread, fermented red onion and gem lettuce. White chocolate, lemon yoghurt and wood sorrel ice cream.

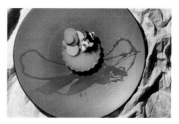

An unassuming-looking restaurant decorated in neutral tones and hung with huge cotton pendant lights. Classically based cooking combines French and Finnish influences to produce robust, satisfying dishes with a subtle modern edge. Choose 4-7 courses; the menu is presented verbally and changes almost daily.

GRÖN ✿

FINNISH • NEIGHBOURHOOD • INTIMATE

Albertinkatu 36 ✉ 00180 PLAN: B2
Ⓜ Kammpi
TEL. 050 3289181 – www.restaurantgron.com
Closed 22 December-6 January, Sunday and Monday
Menu 58€ (dinner only) (booking essential) (tasting menu only)

Chef:
Toni Kostian

Specialities:
Lamb with milk, herbs and summer flowers. Potatoes with spring onion, fermented white asparagus and crayfish broth. Blueberries with woodruff parfait.

A warmly run restaurant where the open kitchen is the focal point and the chefs bring the dishes to the table to explain them. Cooking has a satisfying earthiness and clever use is made of both fresh and fermented ingredients, with vegetables given equal billing with meat or fish. Natural wines are well-chosen.

OLO ✿

MODERN CUISINE • DESIGN • CONTEMPORARY DÉCOR

  ♿ 🅰️🅲️ 🔄

Pohjoisesplanadi 5 ✉ 00170 PLAN: C2
Ⓜ Kaisaneimi
TEL. 010 3206250 – www.olo-ravintola.fi
Closed Christmas, Easter, midsummer, Sunday and Monday
Menu 121€ (dinner only and lunch in December) (tasting menu only) (booking essential)

Chef:
Jari Vesivalo

Specialities:
Pike-perch with caviar and wasabi. Cod, butter sauce and white asparagus juice. Liquorice mousse, beetroot and blackcurrant leaf ice cream.

An attractive harbourside townhouse plays host to this cool, minimalist restaurant, whose four rooms have a delightfully understated feel. Local meats such as moose and elk feature in exciting, innovative dishes which are packed with flavour. Dinner arrives in up to 18 servings.

ORA ✿

MODERN CUISINE • CHIC • COSY

Huvilakatu 28A ✉ 00150 PLAN: C3
TEL. 040 0959440 – www.orarestaurant.fi
Closed 20 June-18 July, Christmas-New Year, Easter, 3rd week
February, 1 week September-October and Sunday-Tuesday
Menu 89€ (dinner only) (tasting menu only) (booking essential)

Chef:
Sasu Laukkonen

Specialities:
White fish, kohlrabi with
horseradish and hyssop. Pork neck
with sunflower and cider sauce.
Meadowsweet flower parfait,
tomato, redcurrants and roses.

This small, intimate restaurant is run by chef-owner Sasu Laukkonen.
The cooking focuses on local ingredients and uses modern techniques
to enhance classic Finnish flavours. Dishes are served and explained
by the chefs themselves.

PALACE ✿

MODERN CUISINE • ELEGANT • DESIGN   ⟨ & AC ⇔

Eteläranta 10 (10th floor) ✉ 00130 PLAN: C2
Ⓜ Rautatientori
TEL. 050 5020718 – www.palacerestaurant.fi
Closed Easter, July, 22 December-8 January and Saturday-Monday
Menu 62/169€ (tasting menu only)

Specialities:
Poached turbot, Jerusalem
artichokes and white Alba truffle.
Loin of venison with baked swede
and juniper. Lemon & liquorice.

On the 10th floor of a modernist building constructed in 1952 for
the Olympic Games, with a sleek interior and harbourside views.
Sophisticated, well balanced and beautifully presented dishes from
a highly experienced Finnish chef, with luxurious ingredients in
harmonious combinations of texture and flavour.

BOULEVARD SOCIAL 😀

MEDITERRANEAN CUISINE • FASHIONABLE   🚻 🛜 A/C

Bulevardi 6 ✉ 00120 **PLAN: C2**
Ⓜ Rautatientori
TEL. 010 3229387 – www.boulevardsocial.fi
Closed Christmas, midsummer and Sunday

Menu 29/57€ – Carte 30/51€

Owned by the same people as next door Gaijin, this lively, informal restaurant offers an accessible range of authentic North African, Turkish and Eastern Mediterranean dishes; try the set or tasting menus to experience a cross-section of them all. If they're fully booked, ask for a seat at the counter.

FARANG 😀

SOUTH EAST ASIAN • SIMPLE • INTIMATE   🚻 A/C 🔄

Ainonkatu 3 (inside the Kunsthalle) ✉ 00100 **PLAN: B2**
Ⓜ Kamppi
TEL. 010 3229385 – www.farang.fi
Closed Christmas, midsummer, Easter, last 3 weeks July, Saturday lunch, Sunday and Monday

Menu 32/64€ – Carte 39/72€

This stylish, modern restaurant is housed in the Kunsthalle art centre. One room is decorated with large photos of Thai scenes and has communal tables; the other is more intimate and furnished in red, black and grey. Zesty, harmonious dishes take their influences from Vietnam, Thailand and Malaysia.

GAIJIN ☺

ASIAN • FASHIONABLE   ♿ 🛁 A/C

Bulevardi 6 ✉ 00120 PLAN: C2
Ⓜ Rautatientori
TEL. 010 3229386 – www.gaijin.fi
Closed Christmas, midsummer and lunch Saturday-Monday
Menu 35/64€ – Carte 33/79€ (booking essential)

Gaijin comes with dark, contemporary décor, a buzzing atmosphere,
attentive service and an emphasis on sharing. Its experienced owners
offer boldly flavoured, skilfully presented modern takes on Japanese,
Korean and Northern Chinese recipes. The tasting menus are a great
way to sample the different cuisines.

JORD ☺

FINNISH • SIMPLE • FASHIONABLE   A/C

Kortteli, Urho Kekkosenkatu 1 (5th Floor) ✉ 00100 PLAN: B2
Ⓜ Kamppi
TEL. 040 5828100 – www.restaurantjord.fi
Closed Christmas, Easter, Sunday and bank holidays
Menu 30/52€ – Carte 33/49€

The bright baby sister to Ask sits in a food court on the 5th floor
of a shopping centre, surrounded by other eateries. Behind a large
counter, the chefs prepare flavoursome, uncomplicated dishes using
largely organic produce. The crockery and glassware are made locally
and the service is warm and friendly.

ATELJÉ FINNE 🍴

MODERN CUISINE • BISTRO • FAMILY ⒶⒸ

Arkadiankatu 14 ✉ 00100 PLAN: B2
Ⓜ Kamppi
TEL. 010 2818242 – www.ateljefinne.fi
Closed Christmas, Easter Monday, midsummer, Saturdays
in July and Sunday

Carte 45/66€ (dinner only)

This is the old studio of sculptor Gunnar Finne, who worked here
for over 30 years. Local art decorates the small bistro-style dining
rooms set over three levels. Regional dishes are given subtle modern
and international twists.

BRONDA 🍴

MODERN CUISINE • FASHIONABLE • BRASSERIE ♿ ⒶⒸ ♨

Eteläesplanadi 20 ✉ 00101 PLAN: C2
Ⓜ Rautatientori
TEL. 010 3229388 – www.ravintolabronda.fi
Closed Christmas, midsummer and Sunday

Menu 32/54€ – Carte 31/83€

The floor to ceiling windows of this old furniture showroom flood it
with light. Enjoy cocktails and snacks at the bar or comforting, boldly
flavoured, Mediterranean sharing plates in the brasserie. Each dish
arrives as it's ready.

CHAPTER

MODERN CUISINE • FRIENDLY • INTIMATE

Aleksanterinkatu 22 ✉ 00170 PLAN: C2
Ⓜ Kaisaniemi
TEL. 050 3564875 – www.chapter.fi
Closed 1 week midsummer, 24-27 December, 1-3 January, Saturday
lunch, Sunday, Monday and dinner Tuesday
Menu 29/84€ (surprise menu only) (booking essential)

Friendly restaurant overlooking the cathedral in the old town and
serving a 3 course lunch menu and 5,7 or 10 course dinner menus.
Skilled, highly original cooking with good use of textural contrasts;
most of the vegetables come from a biodynamic farm in which they
hold shares.

EMO

MODERN CUISINE • FASHIONABLE • INTIMATE

Kluuvikatu 2 ✉ 00100 PLAN: C2
Ⓜ Rautatientori
TEL. 010 5050900 – www.emo-ravintola.fi
Closed Christmas, New Year, Easter Monday, midsummer,
Saturday lunch and Sunday
Menu 39/54€ – Carte 45/74€

Expect modern cooking showcasing original combinations of flavours
and textures, along with a broad range of European influences. It's a
stylish, intimate restaurant run in a friendly and relaxed manner, and it
benefits from a large pavement terrace on a pleasant pedestrianised
street.

GARDEN BY OLO ⸾○

MODERN CUISINE • SIMPLE   [A/C]

Pohjoisesplanadi 5 (Entrance on Helenankatu 2) ⊠ 00170
PLAN: C2
TEL. 010 3206250 – www.olo-ravintola.fi
Closed July, 24-25 December, 2-15 January, Sunday and Monday
Menu 49/65€ – Carte 55/63€ (dinner only) (booking essential)

The casual addendum to Olo occupies a glass-roofed inner courtyard
and has a feeling of openness. The menu has a light, modern style and
some occasional Asian notes; some dishes are designed for sharing.
The cocktails are popular.

GROTESK ⸾○

MEATS AND GRILLS • FASHIONABLE • BRASSERIE 🛖 [A/C] ⟐

Ludviginkatu 10 ⊠ 00130 PLAN: C2
Ⓜ Rautatientori
TEL. 010 4702100 – www.grotesk.fi
Closed Easter, 21-23 June, 24-26 December, 1 January, Sunday and
Monday
Menu 49€ – Carte 41/65€ (dinner only)

A smart, buzzy restaurant behind an impressive 19C façade.
It comprises a fashionable cocktail bar, a wine bar serving interesting
small plates, and a chic dining room which is decorated in black, white
and red and specialises in steaks.

CENTRE

INARI ⊪○

CREATIVE • RUSTIC • NEIGHBOURHOOD

Albertinkatu 19a ✉ 00120 PLAN: B3
TEL. 050 5148155 – www.ravintolainari.fi
Closed Sunday-Tuesday
Menu 70€ (dinner only) (surprise menu only) (booking essential)

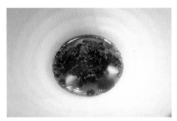 

Hottest ticket in town is this relaxed restaurant, owned and run by Noma alumnus, Kim Mikkola. The set 7 course tasting menu offers Nordic cuisine with Asian influences to the fore and the ambitious, mostly plant-based dishes are well presented and full of flavour.

JUURI ⊪○

TRADITIONAL CUISINE • BISTRO • INTIMATE

Korkeavuorenkatu 27 ✉ 00130 PLAN: C2
TEL. 09 635732 – www.juuri.fi
Closed 23-27 December and midsummer
Carte 39/64€

A friendly bistro with colourful décor and a rustic feel. The focus here is on sharing: small, tapas-style plates showcase organic produce and classic Finnish recipes are given a modern makeover. They brew their own beer in the cellar.

MURU ⅈℹ

MODERN CUISINE • NEIGHBOURHOOD • TRENDY   🕸 ⒶⒸ

Fredrikinkatu 41 ✉ 00120 PLAN: B2
Ⓜ Kamppi
TEL. 0300 472335 – www.murudining.fi
Closed Christmas, New Year, Easter, 1 May, midsummer, Sunday,
Monday and bank holidays
Menu 52€ – Carte 46/52€ (dinner only) (booking essential)

The charming team really enhance your experience at this cosy little
bistro. It's a quirky place, with a wine bottle chandelier, a bar made
from old wine boxes and a high level wine cellar. A blackboard lists
snacks and around 7 main dishes but most diners choose the 4 course
daily menu with a Gallic base.

NATURA ⅈℹ

FINNISH • NEIGHBOURHOOD • DESIGN

Iso Roobertinkatu 11 ✉ 00120 PLAN: C2
TEL. 040 6891111 – www.restaurantnatura.com
Closed July, 23-26 December, 21-23 June, Monday and Tuesday
Menu 39/89€ – Carte 22/41€ (dinner only) (booking essential)

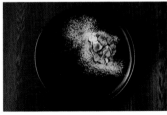

Carefully chosen ingredients are bound together in appealing
seasonal small plates at this intimate restaurant. Techniques mix the
old and the new and dishes are full of colour. Go for the 'Classic' menu,
accompanied by a pure wine.

CENTRE

NOKKA 🍴

MODERN CUISINE • ROMANTIC • RUSTIC

Kanavaranta 7F ✉ 00160 PLAN: D2
TEL. 09 61285600 – www.ravintolanokka.fi
Closed Christmas, Easter, lunch July, Saturday lunch and Sunday
Menu 59/69€ – Carte 42/75€

A huge anchor and propeller mark out this harbourside warehouse and inside, three high-ceilinged rooms juxtapose brick with varnished wood. A glass wall allows you to watch farm ingredients being prepared in a modern Finnish style.

PASSIO 🍴

MODERN CUISINE • FRIENDLY • NEIGHBOURHOOD

Kalevankatu 13 ✉ 00100 PLAN: B2
Ⓜ Kamppi
TEL. 020 7352040 – www.passiodining.fi
Closed Christmas, midsummer, lunch Monday, Tuesday, Saturday and Sunday
Menu 30/52€

Exposed ducts, dimly lit lamps and leather-topped tables give Passio a faux industrial feel. Modern cooking showcases regional ingredients and flavours are well-defined. It's run by a local brewer, so be sure to try the artisan beers.

PASTIS ||○

CLASSIC FRENCH • BISTRO • NEIGHBOURHOOD

Pieni Roobertinkatu 2 ⊠ 00130 **PLAN: C2**
TEL. 0300 472336 – www.pastis.fi
Closed Christmas-New Year, Easter, midsummer, 2 November,
Sunday and lunch Monday and lunch in July

Menu 29€ (lunch) – Carte 40/54€ (booking essential)

The clue is in the name: they serve classic French dishes, alongside
several different brands of pastis. It's a popular place, so there's
always a lively atmosphere. Come for Saturday brunch or have a
private meal in Petit Pastis.

RAGU ||○

MODERN CUISINE • DESIGN • CHIC

Ludviginkatu 3-5 ⊠ 00130 **PLAN: C2**
Ⓜ Rautatientori
TEL. 09 596659 – www.ragu.fi
Closed Christmas, Easter, midsummer and Sunday

Menu 45/57€ – Carte 48/56€ (dinner only)

Finland's famed seasonal ingredients are used in unfussy Italian
recipes and the welcoming service and lively atmosphere also have
something of an Italian feel. Choose the weekly 'Chef's Menu' to
sample the latest produce. Vegetarian/vegan options available.

SALUTORGET ⁏○

INTERNATIONAL • BRASSERIE • ELEGANT   ♿ Ⓐ︎Ⓒ︎

Pohjoisesplanadi 15 ✉ 00170 PLAN: C2
Ⓜ Kaisaniemi
TEL. 09 61285950 – www.salutorget.fi
Closed Christmas, Easter, midsummer, Sunday and Bank holidays
Menu 36/44€ – Carte 35/57€

An old bank, located on the esplanade; now an elegant restaurant with impressive columns and attractive stained glass. The classic, brasserie-style menu has global influences. Enjoy afternoon tea in the plush cocktail bar.

SAVOY ⁏○

MODERN CUISINE • ELEGANT • HISTORIC   🏵 ⪕ 🏠 Ⓐ︎Ⓒ︎ ⟨⟩

Eteläesplanadi 14 (8th floor) ✉ 00130 PLAN: C2
Ⓜ Kaisaniemi
TEL. 09 61285300 – www.ravintolasavoy.fi
Closed 23-30 December, Easter, Saturday lunch and Sunday
Menu 63€ (lunch) – Carte 67/94€

Opened in 1937, this local institution offers impressive views from its 8th floor setting and retains much of its original charm. The updated classics are prepared in an assured, modern style using a blend of influences. Dinner is an intimate affair, complete with pianist.

SPIS †○

MODERN CUISINE • NEIGHBOURHOOD • BISTRO

Kasarmikatu 26 ⊠ 00130 **PLAN: C2**
TEL. 045 3051211 – www.spis.fi
Closed Sunday, Monday and bank holidays
Menu 57/77€ (dinner only) (tasting menu only) (booking essential)

An intimate restaurant seating just 18; the décor is 'faux derelict', with exposed brick and plaster walls. Creative, flavoursome cooking features Nordic flavours in attractive, imaginative combinations. Most dishes are vegetable-based.

TOCA †○

MODERN CUISINE • TRENDY

Unioninkatu 18 ⊠ 00130 **PLAN: C2**
TEL. 044 2379922 – www.toca.fi
Closed July, 23 December-7 January, Sunday and Monday
Menu 45/65€ (dinner only) (tasting menu only) (booking essential)

A passionately run, popular little bistro with a modest, unfinished look. Dinner offers a 3 or 5 set course menu; cooking is an original mix of Italian simplicity and Finnish modernity.

VENTUNO ⁏○

ITALIAN • NEIGHBOURHOOD • OSTERIA ♿ A/C

Korkeavuorenkatu 21 ⊠ 00130 PLAN: C2
TEL. 010 3229395 – www.ventuno.fi
Closed 24-26 December and midsummer
Carte 42/73€

Buzzy, modern day osteria open from early morning for coffee
and pastries; sit in the area next to the glass-fronted wine cabinet.
Authentic Italian dishes cover all the regions of Italy and are unfussy,
full-flavoured and perfect for sharing. The all-Italian wine list is a
labour of love.

VINKKELI ⁏○

CLASSIC CUISINE • ELEGANT • ROMANTIC A/C

Pieni Roobertinkatu 8 ⊠ 00130 PLAN: C2
TEL. 029 1800222 – www.ravintolavinkkeli.fi
Closed 21 December-7 January, 18-22 April, lunch 24 June-18
August, Saturday lunch, Sunday and Monday
Menu 32/56€ – Carte dinner 48/56€

A genuinely charming restaurant. The elegant, high-ceilinged room
is smartly laid out and run by a delightful team, whose attentive and
personable service will make you want to become a regular. The well-
judged cooking is a pleasing mix of the modern and the traditional.

KÄMP

GRAND LUXURY • CLASSIC • HISTORIC

Pohjoisesplanadi 29 ✉ 00100 PLAN: C2
Ⓜ Kaisaniemi
TEL. 09 576111 – www.hotelkamp.com
179 rm – 🛉 220/700€ 🛉🛉 220/700€, ⬚ 32€ – 7 suites

The grand façade, columned interior and impressive staircase point back to this luxurious hotel's 19C roots and the classically furnished bedrooms follow suit; the superb spa, meanwhile, adds a modern touch. The chic bar serves an excellent selection of champagne and cocktails, while for dining, there's a bustling brasserie with an appealing global menu.

CROWNE PLAZA HELSINKI

BUSINESS • CHAIN • CONTEMPORARY

Mannerheimintie 50 ✉ 00260 PLAN: A1
TEL. 09 25210000 – www.crowneplaza-helsinki.fi
349 rm ⬚ – 🛉 140/175€ 🛉🛉 140/175€ – 4 suites

A spacious hotel specialising in conferences. Comfy, up-to-date bedrooms have good facilities and city or lake views; the higher the floor, the better the grade. Pay a visit to the huge basement fitness club and spa, then make for the warm, welcoming restaurant which serves Mediterranean cuisine.

HILTON HELSINKI STRAND

BUSINESS • LUXURY • CLASSIC

≼ 🏠 🕭 🖼 🛝 🕭 AC 🖼 🚗

John Stenbergin Ranta 4 ✉ 00530 PLAN: C1
Ⓜ Hakaniemi
TEL. 09 39351 – www.hilton.com
190 rm – 🛉 130/360€ 🛉🛉 165/395€, ☕ 22€ – 7 suites

This spacious waterfront hotel has a classical 1980s design, an impressive atrium and an 8th floor fitness and relaxation centre; take in the view from the gym or pool. Smartly kept bedrooms boast marble bathrooms – ask for a room overlooking the water. The restaurant offers global classics and local specialities.

ST. GEORGE

LUXURY • DESIGN • PERSONALISED

🏠 🕭 🖼 🕸 🛝 🕭 AC 🖼

Yrjönkatu 13 ✉ 00120 PLAN: C2
Ⓜ Rautatienori
TEL. 09 42460011 – www.stgeorgehelsinki.com
153 rm ☕ – 🛉 150/500€ 🛉🛉 175/525€ – 1 suite

An impressive property with a striking classical façade and a notable collection of modern art. Spacious wintergarden lounge, café-cum-bakery and a tranquil, modern spa. Understated Scandinavian bedrooms with the occasional Italian touch. Andrea restaurant for a blend of Finnish and Anatolian cuisine.

CLARION H.HELSINKI

CHAIN • BUSINESS • DESIGN

Tyynenmerenkatuz 2 ✉ 00220 PLAN: B3
Ⓜ Ruoholahti
TEL. 010 8503820 - www.nordicchoicehotels.fi
425 rm - 106/475€ 106/475€ - 16 suites

This smart skyscraper sits to the west of the city - take in the stunning view from the cool modern bedrooms, the 16th floor gym, the outdoor swimming pool or the Sky Bar. Meeting rooms are housed within a warehouse dating from 1937. The stylish ground floor bistro has a subtle American theme.

GLO HOTEL KLUUVI

LUXURY • MODERN • DESIGN

Kluuvikatu 4 ✉ 00100 PLAN: C2
Ⓜ Kaisaniemi
TEL. 010 3444400 - www.glohotels.fi
184 rm - 144/284€ 144/300€ - 6 suites

A stylish hotel on a fashionable shopping street; a boutique sister to next door Kämp, whose spa it shares. Spacious bedrooms have a contemporary look and come with smart glass shower rooms. There's also a lively bar-lounge and a fashionable restaurant serving cuisine from around the globe.

HAVEN

BUSINESS • LUXURY • MODERN

❀ ⅃ ℻ AC ⅍

Unioninkatu 17 ✉ 00130 PLAN: C2
TEL. 09 681930 – www.hotelhaven.fi
137 rm ⅏ – ♦ 215/369€ ♦♦ 233/387€

A former city centre office block is home to this elegant hotel.
Colourful modern bedrooms come with high ceilings, top quality
furnishings and a plush feel. Extensive breakfasts are served in an
impressive room. Snacks and light dishes are offered in the two cosy
bars and they also have a great rum selection.

KLAUS K

LUXURY • DESIGN • PERSONALISED

❀ ⅏ ℻ AC ⅍

Bulevardi 2/4 ✉ 00120 PLAN: C2
Ⓜ Rautatientori
TEL. 020 7704703 – www.klauskhotel.com
171 rm ⅏ – ♦ 120/320€ ♦♦ 140/640€

The Kalevala – a 19C work of poetry based on Finnish folklore – leads
the design at this striking hotel, from the mosaic fish in the bar to the
graffiti panelled corridors and stylish bedrooms. The Sky Loft rooms
are particularly sumptuous.

LILLA ROBERTS

BUSINESS • DESIGN • PERSONALISED

Pieni Roobertinkatu 1-3 ✉ 00130 **PLAN: C2**
TEL. 09 6899880 - www.lillaroberts.fi
130 rm - 150/210€ 170/220€ - 1 suite

This building was designed in 1908 by one of Finland's top architects and was originally head office for the city's energy works. The smart, designer interior uses dark colours and is centred around the concept of 'hygge' (enjoying the simple things in life). The elegant restaurant serves an appealing menu.

RADISSON BLU PLAZA

BUSINESS • CHAIN • CONTEMPORARY

Mikonkatu 23 ✉ 00100 **PLAN: C2**
Ⓜ Kaisaniemi
TEL. 020 1234703 - www.radissonblu.com/plazahotel-helsinki
302 rm - 120/389€ 135/405€, 25€ - 1 suite

An elegant 20C building set close to the station and completed by a more modern wing. Well-equipped bedrooms come in a choice of modern or classic styles and many have 3D TVs. The bar is a fashionable spot and the large restaurant - unusually set over several rooms - offers five different types of cuisine.

TORNI

BUSINESS • ART DÉCO • ELEGANT

Yrjönkatu 26 ✉ 00100 PLAN: B2
Ⓜ Rautatientori
TEL. 020 1234604 – www.sokoshoteltorni.fi
152 rm ⬜ – 🛏 145/280€ 🛏🛏 180/280€ – 6 suites

A delightful early 20C hotel with a palpable sense of history.
Bedrooms come in 'Art Deco', 'Art Nouveau' and 'Functionalist' styles
– the latter, in the 11 storey tower, have glass-walled bathrooms. The
top floor bar has a terrace and superb city views; the restaurant offers
traditional Finnish cuisine.

FABIAN

TOWNHOUSE • CONTEMPORARY • MODERN

Fabiankatu 7 ✉ 00130 PLAN: C2
TEL. 09 61282000 – www.hotelfabian.fi
58 rm – 🛏 126/350€ 🛏🛏 140/450€, ⬜ 22€

A charming boutique hotel close to the harbour. Bedrooms have
stylish black and white themes and smart bathrooms with heated
floors. Enjoy breakfast in the central courtyard in summer –
ingredients are organic or from small producers.

GLO HOTEL ART

TOWNHOUSE • BUSINESS • MODERN

Lönnrotinkatu 29 ✉ 00180 PLAN: B3
Ⓜ Kamppi
TEL. 010 3444100 – www.glohotels.fi
171 rm ☕ – ♦ 84/233€ ♦♦ 88/250€

Sited in the heart of the lively Design District: a 1903 art nouveau castle with modern extensions and its own art collection. Chic bedrooms were styled by Finnish designers and come in three sizes. You can borrow everything from bicycles to paints and brushes. A Nordic grill menu is served in the old cellars.

KATAJANOKKA

HISTORIC • PERSONALISED • VINTAGE

Merikasarminkatu 1A ✉ 00160 PLAN: D2
TEL. 09 686450 – www.hotelkatajanokka.fi
106 rm ☕ – ♦ 130/250€ ♦♦ 140/400€

A pleasantly restored, late 19C prison where they have retained the original staircases and high ceilinged corridors. The old cells are now comfortable, well-equipped bedrooms with modern bathrooms. The traditional cellar restaurant features a preserved prison cell and serves traditional Finnish cuisine.

ALBERT

BUSINESS • CONTEMPORARY • PERSONALISED

安 も 柳 AC

Albertinkatu 30 ✉ 00180 **PLAN: B3**
TEL. 0201234638 – www.sokoshotels.fi
Closed Christmas
95 rm ☲ – ♦ 129/185€ ♦♦ 144/200€

An unassuming 19C building with a contrastingly cosy interior. Good-sized contemporary bedrooms are well-equipped and come with Nordic furnishings and up-to-date bathrooms. Have drinks in the welcoming open-plan lounge-bar, then head to the trattoria-style restaurant for a selection of Italian classics.

RIVOLI JARDIN

TOWNHOUSE • COSY • PERSONALISED

も 柳

Kasarmikatu 40 ✉ 00130 **PLAN: C2**
TEL. 09681500 – www.rivoli.fi
Closed Christmas
55 rm ☲ – ♦ 100/240€ ♦♦ 120/440€

A small, city centre oasis hidden away off a courtyard, with an intimate conservatory lounge, and a sauna and meeting room tucked away in the cellar. Bedrooms are cosy and individually decorated; the top floor rooms have terraces.

HILTON HELSINKI AIRPORT

BUSINESS • CHAIN • MODERN

Lentàjànkuja 1 (North: 19 km by A 137) ✉ 01530
TEL. 09 73220 – www.hilton.com
330 rm – ♦ 99/370€ ♦♦ 109/400€, ☕ 27€ – 5 suites

3mins from the international terminal (T2): a spacious glass hotel
with a relaxed ambience and a large conference capacity. Well-
soundproofed bedrooms boast locally designed furniture, good
facilities and large bathrooms – some have saunas. The stylish
restaurant serves Finnish and international cuisine.

KASKIS ⓘO

MODERN CUISINE • FRIENDLY • NEIGHBOURHOOD   A/C

Kaskenkatu 6A ✉ 20700
TEL. 044 7230200 – www.kaskis.fi
Closed 3 weeks Christmas-January, 2 weeks midsummer, Sunday
and Monday
Menu 55/66€ (dinner only) (booking essential)

A very popular glass-fronted restaurant that always has a lively,
fun atmosphere. The kitchen uses good ingredients and dishes are
brought to the table by the chefs who explain their quite elaborate
construction in full.

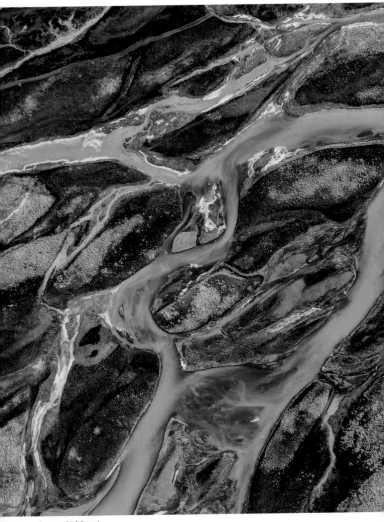

ICELAND

BIB GOURMAND

REYKJAVIK

ICELAND

Europe's youngest landmass is a country of extremes; a dramatic wilderness where volcanic springs sit beside vast glaciers and long summer days are offset by dark winters. Its largest city, Reykjavik, lays claim to being the world's most northern capital and its settlement by a Norseman over 1100 years ago is recounted in the Icelandic Sagas.

Two thirds of Icelanders live in Reykjavik, in low, colourful buildings designed to fend off the North Atlantic winds and brighten spirits through the long, dark nights. Other buildings

echo nature itself: the geometric shapes of the Hallgrímskirkja Church – whose soaring tower keeps watch over the city – mirror the lava flows, while the Harpa Concert Hall is cleverly designed to reflect both the city and nature – its cascading LEDs alluding to the incredible spectacle of the Aurora Borealis.

The historic city centre, known as 101, lies between the harbour and an inland lake, and is a bustling, bohemian place filled with independent boutiques and fashionable bars. Head out further east and you can discover the secrets of the Blue Lagoon's healing thermal waters and the Golden Circle, which comprises three of Iceland's greatest natural wonders: the Þingvellir National Park (where you can walk between two tectonic plates); the Haukadalur Geothermal Field with its geysers and mud pools; and the spectacular Gullfoss Waterfall – the largest in Europe.

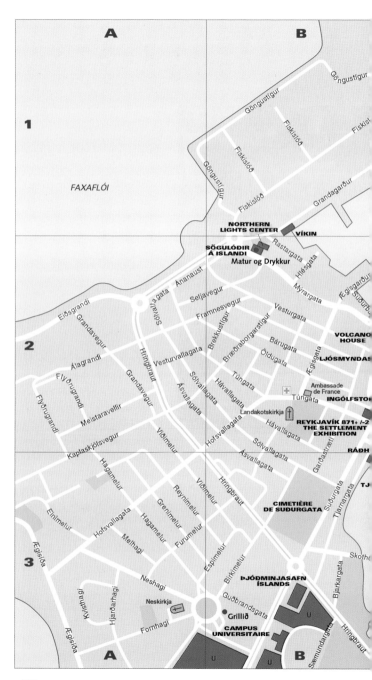

A

B

1

FAXAFLÓI

NORTHERN LIGHTS CENTER   **VÍKIN**

Rastargata

SÖGULÓDIR Á ISLANDI

Matur og Drykkur

Göngustígur

Göngustígur

Fiskislóð

Fiskislóð

Fiskislóð

Göngustígur

Grandagarður

Hlésgata

Ægisgarður

Suðurbu

Myrargata

Ananaust

Seljavegur

Silfavar gata

Eiðsgrandi

Grandavegur

Framnesvegur

Vesturgata

VOLCANO HOUSE

Brekkustígur

Bræðraborgarstígur

Bárugata

Öldugata

Ægisgata

LJÓSMYNDAS

Vesturvallagata

Álagrandi

Grandavegur

Túngata

Hringbraut

Sólvallagata

Ásvallagata

Hávallagata

Ambassade de France

Túngata

INGÓLFSTO

Landakotskirkja

Flyðrugrandi

Meistaravellir

Viðimelur

Hofsvallagata

Hávallagata

REYKJAVÍK 871+ /-2 THE SETTLEMENT EXHIBITION

Flyðrugrandi

Sólvallagata

Garðastræti

RÁÐH

Kaplaskjólsvegur

Ásvallagata

2

Hagamelur

Viðimelur

Reynimelur

Hringbraut

CIMETIÈRE DE SUDURGATA

Suðurgata

Tjarnargata

TJ

Erimelur

Grenimelur

Hagamelur

Furumelur

Hofsvallagata

Melhagi

Espimelur

Bitrimelur

Ægisíða

Neshagi

ÞJÓÐMINJASAFN ÍSLANDS

Skothú

Bjarkargata

Hringbrau

Ægisíða

Kvistholagi

Hjarðarhagi

Neskirkja

Fornhagi

Guðbrandsgata

• Grillið

CAMPUS UNIVERSITAIRE

U

U

U

Samundargata

3

A

B

Reykjavik Centre

C **D**

0 |————————| 200 m

1

FAXAFLÓI

PORT

HARPA

2

LISTASAFN
REYKJAVÍKUR

KOLAPORTID

Geirsgata

Faxagata

Skúlagata

Sæbraut

Tryggvagata

Hafnarstræti

Ingólfsstræti

Sölvhólsgata

Skúlagata

Sæbraut

ARNARHÓLL

ustursstræti

STJÓRNARRÁDID

ÞJÓDMENNINGARHÚSID

SUN-CRAFT

TURVÖLLUR

▲ Borg

101 ▲

Lækjargata

Laugavegur

ÞJÓDLEIKHÚSID

Lindargata

A-HÚS

Dill

NG

DÓMKIRKJAN

Hverfisgata

Sæbraut

MENNTASKÓLINN

Canopy
by Hilton ▲

Lavatnsstígur

NÝLISTASAFNID

Skúlagata

ÁTRE
NÓ

Laufásvegur

Miðstræti

Þingholtsstræti

Bergstaðastræti

Klapparstígur

ÓX

Laugavegur

Sümac

Grettisgata

Sand

Frakkastígur

Hverfisgata

SÆBRAUT

Snorrabraut

Nostra ●

FRÍKIRKJAN

Óðinsgata

Týsgata

Skólavörðustígur

Njálsgata

Vitastígur

▲ Alda

Grettisgata

Baronsstígur

3

LISTASAFN
ÍSLANDS

Lokastígur

Þórsgata

Njálsgata

Skál! ●

Laugavegur

Hellusund

▲ Holt

Freyjugata

REDASAFN

Grettisgata

Fjölugata

Baldursgata

Bragagata

Bergþórugata

Njálsgata

Laufásvegur

Sóleyjargata

LISTASAFN
EINARS JÓNSSONAR

HALLGRÍMSKIRKJA

Njarðargata

LISTASAFN ASÍ

Mímisvegur

Bergstaðastræti

Baronsstígur

Leifsgata

Egilsgata

C **D**

▲	Hotel
●	Restaurant

SKÁL! 🍴

TRADITIONAL CUISINE • SIMPLE • FRIENDLY   ♿ ⚟

Hlemmur Mathöll, Laugavegur 107 ✉ 101 **PLAN: D3**
TEL. 775 2299 – www.skalrvk.com
Closed 24-25 December and 1 January
Carte 3300/5550 ISK (bookings not accepted)

Counter dining in Iceland's first food market; this is friendly, relaxed and great fun! Modern interpretations of traditional Icelandic dishes are designed for sharing; dishes arrive all at once and are robust, generously sized, full of flavour and good value for money.

DILL 🍴

CREATIVE • RUSTIC • INTIMATE   ⚟ ⚙

Hverfisgötu 12 (Entrance on Ingólfsstræti) ✉ 101 **PLAN: C2**
TEL. 552 1522 – www.dillrestaurant.is
Closed 23 December-1 January and Sunday-Tuesday
Menu 13900 ISK (dinner only) (tasting menu only)
(booking essential)

Resembling an old barn, this small, dimly-lit restaurant has become a favourite destination for New Nordic cooking. The best of the island's larder is prepared at the central counter, where traditional skills blend with modern techniques to produce dishes that are creative, colourful and balanced.

GRILLIÐ ⑩

MODERN CUISINE • CLASSIC DÉCOR • ELEGANT ≼ AC ⇹ P

Radisson Blu Saga Hotel (8th floor), Hagatorg ⊠ 107 PLAN: B3
TEL. 525 9960 – www.grillid.is
Closed Sunday-Tuesday
Menu 12900 ISK (dinner only) (booking essential)

This 'grill room' sits at the top of a hotel and was established over 50 years ago. The unusual ceiling depicts the signs of the zodiac but it's the 360° views that will steal your attention, especially at sunset. The array of imaginatively presented, adventurous Nordic dishes are delivered by a young team.

MATUR OG DRYKKUR ⑩

TRADITIONAL CUISINE • SIMPLE • TRENDY ⅍ ⇹ P

Grandagarður 2 ⊠ 101 PLAN: B2
TEL. 571 8877 – www.maturogdrykkur.is
Closed 24 December, 1 January and Sunday lunch
Menu 3690 ISK (lunch) – Carte 4070/10070 ISK

This simple little eatery is named after an Icelandic cookbook and shares its premises with the Saga Museum. Old recipes are given modern twists, resulting in delicious dishes with a creative edge. The à la carte is supplemented by great value 'Icelandic Snacks', along with various tasting menus at dinner.

NOSTRA ⑪○

MODERN CUISINE • CONTEMPORARY DÉCOR •
DESIGN   ⚐ AK ⑆

Laugavegur 59 (1st floor) ✉ 101 PLAN: D3
TEL. 519 3535 – www.nostrarestaurant.is
Closed 24-25 December, 6-16 January, Sunday and Monday
Menu 8900/13900 ISK – Carte 8970/11970 ISK (dinner only)
(booking essential)

Don't let the exterior of this building put you off; inside the décor
is sleek, modern and minimalistic while the food uses only the very
best seasonal Icelandic produce in strikingly presented dishes with
clarity of flavour and a deft touch. Tasting menus only at weekends.

ÓX ⑪○

MODERN CUISINE • INTIMATE • FRIENDLY   ⑆

Laugavegur 28 ✉ 101 PLAN: C3
www.ox.dinesuperb.com
Closed Sunday-Tuesday
Menu 29000 ISK (dinner only) (surprise menu only)
(booking essential)

A hidden counter dining experience at the back of the lively Sümac.
Cooking is a mix of old and new, with local produce to the fore. Dishes
are original and visually appealing with great flavours. The menu price
includes all drinks and is paid in advance so there's no bill at the end.

SÜMAC ¶⃝

MIDDLE EASTERN • BRASSERIE • TRENDY   ♿ Ⓐ ⅋

Laugavegur 28 ✉ 101 **PLAN: C3**
TEL. 537 9900 – www.sumac.is
Closed 24-25 December, 1 January, lunch Saturday and Sunday
Menu 3850/8700 ISK – Carte 4630/7880 ISK

A lively modern brasserie with on-trend concrete walls, burnished leather banquettes and a charcoal grill. Icelandic ingredients are given a Middle Eastern twist, with influences from North Africa to the Lebanon. Cooking is rustic and full of flavour; go for the sharing meze menus.

VOX ¶⃝

MODERN CUISINE • CONTEMPORARY DÉCOR • ELEGANT   ♿ Ⓐ ⅋ ⇧ Ⓟ

Hilton Reykjavik Nordica Hotel, Suðurlandsbraut 2
(East: 2.75 km by 41) ✉ 108
TEL. 444 5050 – www.vox.is
Menu 4000 ISK – Carte 7350/12030 ISK

A stylish restaurant and bar set off the lobby of the Hilton hotel. At lunch there's a popular hot and cold buffet; at dinner, choices include an à la carte and 'Season' and 'Seafood' tasting menus. Cooking is modern and creative.

101

LUXURY • DESIGN • TRENDY

⇐ ⛏ 𝕸 𝄃𝄂 AC ⇎

Hverfisgata 8-10 ✉ 101 **PLAN: C2**
TEL. 580 0101 – www.101hotel.is
38 rm – ♦ 47900/79900 ISK ♦♦ 59900/108900 ISK, ☕ 2990 ISK

Behind the unassuming façade of the former Social Democratic Party offices, you'll find this sleek design hotel filled with interesting Icelandic art. Stylish monochrome bedrooms have stunning glass bathrooms; choose one with a balcony or a harbour view. The stylish restaurant with its long bar and glass ceiling is the perfect spot to try modern Icelandic cooking.

BORG

LUXURY • ART DÉCO • ELEGANT

⛏ 𝕸 𝄃𝄂 ⇎ 𝄜

Pósthússtræti 11 ✉ 101 **PLAN: C2**
TEL. 551 1440 – www.keahotels.is
99 rm ☕ – ♦ 28000/65000 ISK ♦♦ 35000/67500 ISK – 2 suites

Overlooking Austurvöllur Square is this carefully restored 1930s hotel which combines traditional elegance with modern comforts. Bedrooms encapsulate the art deco era with bespoke furnishings, wooden floors and elegant lines. The bar has a lovely square counter and the restaurant offers Italian comfort food.

CANOPY BY HILTON

BOUTIQUE HOTEL • CONTEMPORARY • TRENDY

⚐ 🚴 🛴 ⇥ 🚴

Smidjustigur 4 ✉ 101 **PLAN: C2/3**
TEL. 528 7000 – www.canopybyhilton.com
112 rm ⌂ – 🛉 16100/36000 ISK 🛉🛉 30000/62000 ISK – 5 suites

The first ever 'Canopy' sits just off the main street. It's a relaxed and stylish home-from-home; grab breakfast in the deli, borrow a bike or take in city views from the top floor terrace. Understated bedrooms feature natural materials, bespoke furniture and quirky artwork. Menus offer creative small plates.

HOLT

FAMILY • CLASSIC • COSY

⇥ 🅿

Bergstaðastræti 37 ✉ 101 **PLAN: C3**
TEL. 552 5700 – www.holt.is
42 rm ⌂ – 🛉 38000/48000 ISK 🛉🛉 38000/48000 ISK – 4 suites

The draw of this family-run hotel is its old world charm and quiet suburban location. The 4th floor bedrooms look out over the city, while the cosy lounge and cocktail bar are great places to appreciate their vast art collection.

SAND

BOUTIQUE HOTEL • DESIGN • ELEGANT

⚡

Laugavegur 34 ✉ 101 **PLAN: D3**
TEL. 519 8090 – www.sandhotel.is
67 rm ☕ – 👤 32000/38950 ISK 👥 36500/43450 ISK – 1 suite

A stylish modern boutique hotel comprising seven townhouses, set in the heart of the city. Bedrooms are understated, with Nordic design touches from Icelandic fabrics to locally produced toiletries. The renowned Sandholt Bakery which adjoins the hotel is a great place for a cinnamon bun and a coffee.

ALDA

BOUTIQUE HOTEL • CONTEMPORARY • TRENDY

⋙ 🛁 ⚡

Laugavegur 66-68 ✉ 101 **PLAN: D3**
TEL. 553 9366 – www.aldahotel.is
88 rm ☕ – 👤 20000/25000 ISK 👥 25000/39000 ISK – 2 suites

At the quieter eastern end of the main shopping street you'll find this fashionable hotel complete with its own barber's shop and a trendy bar offering simple meals. Bedrooms are simply but stylishly furnished with natural materials like Icelandic wool; the 4th floor rooms have balconies with sea views.

MOSS ⅏

MODERN CUISINE • ELEGANT • DESIGN   &⅌ ⪬ ⅌ ⅗ **P**

Retreat at Blue Lagoon Hotel • Nordurljosavegur 11 (Southwest:
50 km of Reykjavik by 41) ⊠ 240
TEL. 420 8700 – www.bluelagoon.com/restaurant/moss

Menu 13900/15900 ISK (dinner only) (tasting menu only)
(bookings essential for non-residents)

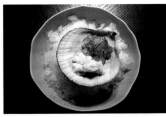

Floor to ceiling windows offer views of the volcanic landscape at
this modern hotel restaurant, where booking is essential for non-
residents. Sit at the chefs table or in one of the sumptuous booths
to enjoy dishes from the 5-7 course tasting menu. Excellent wine list
– ask for a tour of the cellar.

dibrova/iStock

NORWAY

STARS & BIB GOURMAND

OSLO

Norway

Oslo has a lot going for it – and one slight downside: it's one of the world's most expensive cities. It also ranks high when it comes to its standard of living, however, and its position at the head of Oslofjord, surrounded by steep forested hills, is hard to match for drama and beauty. It's a charmingly compact place to stroll round, particularly in the summer, when the daylight hours practically abolish the night and, although it may lack the urban cool of some other Scandinavian cities, it boasts its fair share of trendy clubs and a raft of Michelin Stars. There's a real raft,

too: Thor Hyerdahl's famous Kon-Tiki – one of the star turns in a city that loves its museums. Oslo's uncluttered feel is enhanced by parks and wide streets and, in the winter, there are times when you feel you have the whole place to yourself. Drift into the city by boat and land at the smart harbour of Aker Brygge; to the west lies the charming Bygdøy peninsula, home to museums permeated with the smell of the sea. Northwest is Frogner, with its famous sculpture park, the place where locals hang out on long summer days. The centre of town, the commercial hub, is Karl Johans Gate, bounded at one end by the Royal Palace and at the other by the Cathedral, while further east lie two trendy multicultural areas, Grunerlokka and Grønland, the former also home to the Edvard Munch Museum.

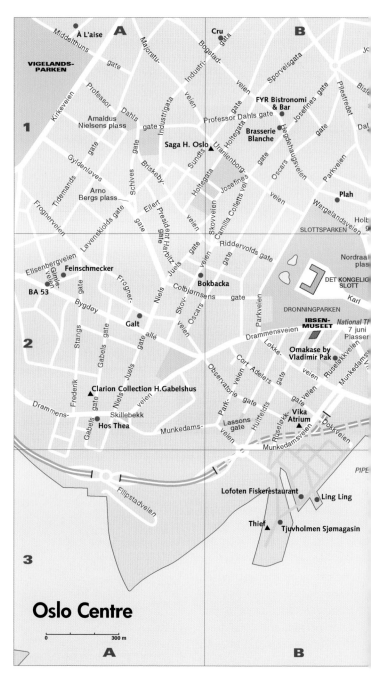

Oslo Centre

0 _____ 300 m

A (top) · **B** (top)

A 1 VIGELANDS-PARKEN · Middelthuns gate · À L'aise · Majorstu- · Professor Dahls gate · Kirkeveien · Amaldus Nielsens plass · Industrigata · Industrivelen · Gyldenløves gate · Tidemands gate · Briskeby- · Schives gate · Arno Bergs plass · Frognerveien · Løvenskiolds gate · Eilert · President Harbitz gate

B 1 Cru gata · Bogstad- · Sporveisgata · Pilestredet · velen · Josefines gate · FYR Bistronomi & Bar · Professor Dahls gate · Brasserie Blanche · Hegdehaugsveien · Oscars gate · Parkveien · Dal · Saga H. Oslo ▲ · Uranienborg · Holtegata · Sundts gate · Josefines velen · Camilla Colletts vei · Skovveien · Plah · Wergelandsveien · Holt · SLOTTSPARKEN · 9 · Bisle · Jo

A 2 Elisenbergveien · Feinschmecker · Gimle- · velen · BA 53 · Bygdøy · Frogner- · gate · Niels Juels gate · Bokbacka · Colbjørnsens gate · Skov- · Galt · gate allé · Oscars velen · Stangs gate · Gabels gate · Juels gate · Frederik · Clarion Collection H. Gabelshus ▲ · Niels Juels veien · Skillebekk · Drammens- · Gabels gate · Hos Thea · Munkedams-

B 2 Riddervolds gate · Nordraa plas · DET KONGELIGE SLOTT · DRONNINGPARKEN · Karl · Parkveien · IBSEN-MUSEET · National Th · 7 juni Plasser · Drammensveien · Lokke- · Omakase by Vladimir Pak · Ruseløkkveien · Munkedams Vi · Cort Adelers · velen · Observatorie- · gate · Park- · Cort Adelers gate · gate velen · Lassons gate · Huitfelds · Ruseløkk · Vika Atrium ▲ · Dokkveien · Munkedamsveien

A 3 Filipstadveien

B 3 PIPE · Lofoten Fiskerestaurant · Ling Ling · Thief ▲ · Tjuvholmen Sjømagasin

A (bottom) · **B** (bottom)

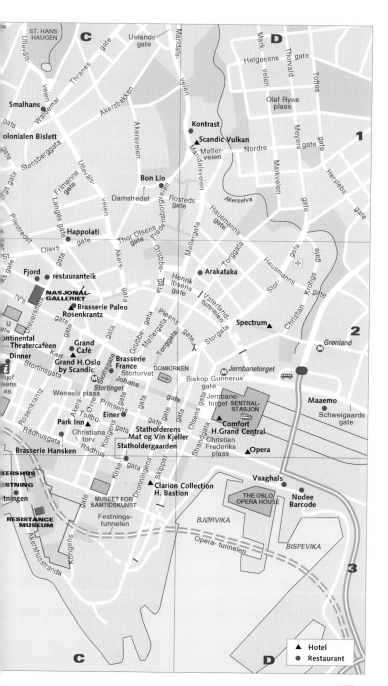

ST. HANS-HAUGEN

C

Uelands gate

D

Mark-

Helgesens gate

Thorvald

Tottes gate

Ullevåls...

Thranes

veien

Waldemar

Uelands gate

Maridals-

veien

Olaf Ryes plass

Meyers gate

Smalhans

gata

Akersbakken

Kontrast

1

olonialen Bislett

Stensberggata

Akersveien

Scandic Vulkan

Møller-veien

Nordre

Markveien

Herslebs gate

gate

Frimanns gate

Langes gate

Ullevåls-veien

Bon Lio

Maridalsveien

Damstredet

Rosteds gate

Akerselva

Hausmanns gate

gata

Happolati

gate

Thor Olsens gate

Frederiks gt.

Møllergata

Torggata

Hausmanns

Krohgs gate

St.

gate

Olavs

Akers-

gata

Henrik Ibsens gate

Arakataka

Stor-

Christian

Fjord ● restauranteik

Grubbe-

Vaterland-tunnelen

NASJONAL-GALLERIET

gata

Pløens gate

Spectrum▲

Brasserie Paleo

Rosenkrantz

Grubbe-gata

Møllergata

Torggata

Storgata

Grønland

IV's

U

ontinental

Theatercaféen

Grand Café

Karl

gata

Storgata

Møllergata

2

Dinner

Grand H.Oslo by Scandic

Brasserie France

DOMKIRKEN

Jernbanetorget

Maaemo

tjof

sens

ss

Stortingsgata

Stortinget

Johans

Stortorvet

Biskop Gunnerus' gate

SENTRAL-STASJON

Schweigaards gate

Rosenkrantz

Wessels plass

Akers-

Prinsens gate

gate

Olsens gate

Jernbane-torget

Rådhusgata

Park Inn▲

Einer ●

gate

Strandgata

Comfort H.Grand Central

Christiania torv

Kongens gate

Statholderens Mat og Vin Kjeller

Christian Frederiks plass

Brasserie Hansken

Rådhus...

Statholdergaarden

▲Opera

KERSHUS

ESTNING

Kirke- gata

Dronningens

Clarion Collection H. Bastion

Vaaghals ●

tningen

Skipper-

THE OSLO OPERA HOUSE

Nodee ●

RESISTANCE MUSEUM

MUSEET FOR SAMTIDSKUNST

Festnings-tunnelen

BJØRVIKA

Barcode

Akershusstranda

Kongens

Opera- tunnelen

BISPEVIKA

3

C

D

▲ Hotel
● Restaurant

137

MAAEMO ✿✿✿

MODERN CUISINE • DESIGN • FASHIONABLE   A/C

Schweigaardsgate 15B ✉ 0191 **PLAN: D2**
Ⓜ Grønland
TEL. 22 17 99 69 – www.maaemo.no
Closed Christmas, Easter and Sunday-Tuesday

Menu 2800 NOK (dinner only and lunch Friday-Saturday)
(tasting menu only) (booking essential)

Chef:
Esben Holmboe Bang

Specialities:
Oysters and aged caviar with
mussel and dill sauce. Reindeer
with preserved plums. Norwegian
strawberries with rhubarb root and
wood sorrel.

Maaemo means 'Mother Earth' and this striking restaurant is all about
connecting with nature. Service is perfectly choreographed and
dishes are brought down from the mezzanine feature kitchen and
finished at the table by the chefs themselves. Innovative, intricate
cooking awakens the senses with sublime flavour combinations –
some dishes take several days to construct.

GALT ✿

MODERN CUISINE • RUSTIC • CHIC   A/C

Frognerveien 12B ✉ 0263 **PLAN: A2**
TEL. 48 51 48 86 – www.galt.no
Closed 22 December-3 January, 20-23 April, Sunday and Monday

Menu 865 NOK – Carte 515/715 NOK (dinner only)

Chef:
Bjørn Svensson

Specialities:
Langoustine, watercress and rye.
Duck with leek, barley and tarragon
sauce. Milk ice cream, blueberries,
chocolate and verbena.

The friends who previously ran Fauna and Oscarsgate have created
this warm, intimate restaurant with an appealingly rustic feel. The
set menu of 6 courses is nicely balanced, flavour combinations have
been well thought through, and the contrast in textures is a particular
strength.

KONTRAST ❀

SCANDINAVIAN • DESIGN • FASHIONABLE   ♿ Ⓐ🄲 ⇔

Maridalsveien 15 ✉ 0178 **PLAN: D1**
TEL. 21 60 01 01 – www.restaurant-kontrast.no
Closed 2 weeks Christmas-New Year, 2 weeks Easter,
Sunday and Monday
Menu 1150/1600 NOK – Carte 595/960 NOK (dinner only)

Chef:
Mikael Svensson
Specialities:
Langoustine served '3 ways' with
rosehip. Mangalitsa pork with Swiss
chard and pickled fennel. Hen's egg
preserved in elderflower syrup.

A modern restaurant with a stark, semi-industrial feel created by a
concrete floor, exposed pipework and an open kitchen. Seasonal,
organic Norwegian produce is used to create refined, original,
full-flavoured dishes whose apparent simplicity often masks their
complex nature. The service is well-paced.

STATHOLDERGAARDEN ❀

CLASSIC CUISINE • INTIMATE • ELEGANT   ⮾ ⇔

Rådhusgata 11 (entrance on Kirkegata) ✉ 0151 **PLAN: C3**
Ⓜ Stortinget
TEL. 22 41 88 00 – www.statholdergaarden.no
Closed 14 July-6 August, 23 December-3 January,
14-23 April, Sunday and bank holidays
Menu 1195 NOK – Carte 1020/1180 NOK (dinner only)
(booking essential)

Chef:
Bent Stiansen
Specialities:
Langoustine, radish, broccoli and
black garlic. Lamb with salsify, kale
and rosemary sauce. Raspberry
with mascarpone and elderflower.

A charming 17C house in the city's heart. Three elegant rooms feature
an array of antiques and curios, and have wonderfully ornate stucco
ceilings hung with chandeliers. Expertly rendered classical cooking
uses seasonal Norwegian ingredients in familiar combinations.
Service is well-versed and willing.

SMALHANS ☻

TRADITIONAL CUISINE • NEIGHBOURHOOD • SIMPLE ⟱

Ullevålsveien 43 ⊠ 0171 PLAN: C1
TEL. 22 69 60 00 – www.smalhans.no
Closed 7-28 July, 22 December-2 January ,17-23 April and lunch
Monday and Tuesday
Menu 450/650 NOK (dinner) – Carte lunch 440/490 NOK
(booking essential at dinner)

A sweet neighbourhood café with friendly staff and an urban feel.
Coffee and homemade cakes are served in the morning, with a short
selection of dishes including soup and a burger on offer between
12pm and 4pm. A daily hot dish is available from 4-6pm, while set
menus and sharing plates are served at dinner.

À L'AISE 🍴

MODERN CUISINE • INTIMATE • ELEGANT   ⊗ AC ⟱

Essendrops gate 6 ⊠ 0368 PLAN: A1
Ⓜ Majorstuen
TEL. 21 05 57 00 – www.alaise.no
Closed 3 weeks July-August, Christmas, Easter, Sunday and
Monday
Carte 960/1245 NOK (dinner only)

This elegant, sophisticated restaurant is run by an engaging,
knowledgeable team. The experienced chef is something of a
Francophile: expect refined Gallic dishes packed with flavour and
crafted from French and Norwegian produce.

ARAKATAKA 🍴○

NORWEGIAN • FASHIONABLE • FRIENDLY   A/C ⇔

Mariboes gate 7 ✉ 0183 **PLAN: D2**
Ⓜ Stortinget
TEL. 23 32 83 00 – www.arakataka.no
Closed July, Christmas-New Year and Easter
Menu 650 NOK – Carte 455/525 NOK (dinner only)

A smart glass-fronted restaurant with a central food bar, an open
kitchen and a buzzy atmosphere. Choose from a concise menu of
seasonal Norwegian small plates – they recommend 3 savoury dishes
plus a dessert per person.

BA 53 🍴○

MODERN CUISINE • FASHIONABLE •
NEIGHBOURHOOD   🛜 A/C ⇔

Bygdoy Allé 53 ✉ 0265 **PLAN: A2**
TEL. 21 42 05 90 – www.ba53.no
Closed July, Christmas, Easter and Sunday
Carte 400/640 NOK (dinner only and Saturday lunch)

A moody cocktail bar combines with a relaxed, softly lit brasserie
to create this stylish neighbourhood hotspot. Menus offer a mix of
Nordic classics and more modern dishes; four per person is ample.

BOKBACKA 🍴

MODERN CUISINE • FASHIONABLE • NEIGHBOURHOOD

Skovveien 15 ✉ 0257 PLAN: A2
TEL. 412 60 144 – www.bokbacka.no
Closed 14 July-11 August, 21 December-3 January, 14-22 April,
Sunday-Monday and bank holidays

Menu 795 NOK (dinner only) (tasting menu only)

A unique 'food bar' with clean, light styling and fun, idiosyncratic
features; most seats are arranged around the open kitchen, with only
4 other tables. Many of the theatrically presented dishes on the set
omakase-style menu have a story.

BON LIO 🍴

MODERN CUISINE • SIMPLE • COSY

Fredensborgveien 42 ✉ 0177 PLAN: C1
TEL. 467 77 212 – www.bonlio.no
Closed 2 weeks July, Christmas, Easter, Sunday and Monday

Menu 865 NOK (dinner only) (surprise menu only) (booking
essential)

A lively, fun gastro-bar in a characterful 200 year old cottage. The
Norwegian owner grew up in Mallorca and showcases local and
imported ingredients in a surprise 12-17 course tapas-style menu.
Spanish beers and wines accompany.

BRASSERIE BLANCHE

FRENCH • COSY • BRASSERIE

Josefinesgate 23 ✉ 0351 **PLAN: B1**
TEL. 23 20 13 10 – www.blanche.no
Closed 9-31 July, 23-26 December and Monday
Menu 395 NOK – Carte 352/595 NOK (dinner only)

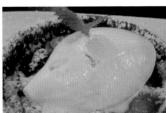

A cosy French restaurant housed in an 18C building which was originally a stable and later spent time as a garage and an interior furnishings store. It has a small front terrace, a bar decorated with wine boxes and a wall made of corks. The chef is a Francophile and creates flavoursome classic French dishes.

BRASSERIE FRANCE

FRENCH • BRASSERIE • TRADITIONAL DÉCOR

Øvre Slottsgate 16 ✉ 0157 **PLAN: C2**
Ⓜ Stortinget
TEL. 23 10 01 65 – www.brasseriefrance.no
Closed 23 December-2 January, Easter, Sunday and lunch Monday
Menu 370/495 NOK – Carte 480/730 NOK

This lively Gallic brasserie in a pedestrianised shopping street has several private dining rooms. Brasserie classics range from bouillabaisse to steak frites; for dessert, choose from the 'eat-as-much-as-you-like' pastry trolley.

BRASSERIE HANSKEN 🍴

MODERN CUISINE • FAMILY • BRASSERIE

Akersgate 2 ✉ 0158 PLAN: C2
Ⓜ Stortinget
TEL. 22 42 60 88 – www.brasseriehansken.no
Closed Christmas-New Year, Monday in July and Sunday

Carte 595/775 NOK

A delightfully traditional brasserie, centrally located by City Hall, with various charming dining areas and a fantastic terrace. Classical cooking follows the seasons and mixes French and Scandic influences; seafood is a speciality.

BRASSERIE PALEO 🍴

SCANDINAVIAN • DESIGN • BRASSERIE

Hotel Rosenkrantz • Rosenkrantz gate 1 ✉ 0159 PLAN: C2
Ⓜ National Theatrer
TEL. 23 315 5 80 – www.brasseriepaleo.no
Closed early July-early August, Christmas, Easter and Sunday

Carte 545/595 NOK

With a name which reflects its philosophy, and a contemporary urban style, this is not your typical hotel restaurant. Watch the chefs prepare attractive modern Scandinavian dishes in the open kitchen. Service is professional and friendly.

CRU ⁑○

NORWEGIAN • WINE BAR • TRENDY

Ingelbrecht, Knudssøns gate 1 ⊠ 0365 PLAN: B1
Ⓜ Majorstuen
TEL. 23 98 98 98 – www.cru.no
Closed 1 July-2 August, 22 December-2 January, Easter and Sunday

Menu 595 NOK – Carte 500/530 NOK
(dinner only and Saturday lunch)

Upstairs, in the rustic restaurant, they serve a set 4 course menu with inventive British touches and 4 optional extra courses. Downstairs, in the wine bar, you can enjoy everything from nibbles to a full meal from the à la carte.

DINNER ⁑○

CHINESE • DESIGN • ELEGANT

Stortingsgata 22 ⊠ 0161 PLAN: C2
Ⓜ National Theatret
TEL. 23 10 04 66 – www.dinner.no
Closed 24 December-2 January , Easter and Sunday lunch

Menu 195/399 NOK – Carte 310/475 NOK

An intimate restaurant on the central square, close to the National Theatre. A black frosted glass façade masks a smart split-level interior. The kitchen focuses on Sichuan cuisine, with artfully presented dim sum at lunch.

EINER ⸮O

MODERN CUISINE • FRIENDLY • DESIGN ♿

Prinsens gate 18 ✉ 0152 **PLAN: C2**
Ⓜ Stortinget
TEL. 22 41 55 55 – www.restauranteiner.no
Closed 2 weeks July, Christmas, Easter, Sunday and Monday

Menu 650/850 NOK (dinner only) (tasting menu only)
(booking essential)

Personally run restaurant serving 4 and 6 course tasting menus with an emphasis on Norwegian seafood. Understated, full-flavoured modern dishes use original combinations alongside traditional techniques such as fermenting, pickling and smoking. The wine matches are well worth choosing.

FEINSCHMECKER ⸮O

TRADITIONAL CUISINE • CLASSIC DÉCOR • NEIGHBOURHOOD

Balchens gate 5 ✉ 0265 **PLAN: A2**
TEL. 22 12 93 80 – www.feinschmecker.no
Closed 3 weeks summer, Christmas, Easter and Sunday

Menu 895 NOK – Carte 665/1000 NOK (dinner only)

This long-standing restaurant – run by a charming team – has a cosy, welcoming atmosphere and a loyal local following. The well-presented dishes are classically based, with French influences. Wine pairings are available.

FESTNINGEN ‖○

MODERN CUISINE • BRASSERIE •
FASHIONABLE

Myntgata 9 ⊠ 0151 **PLAN: C3**
TEL. 22 83 3100 – www.festningenrestaurant.no
Closed 22 December-4 January, 10 days Easter and Sunday

Menu 315/595 NOK – Carte 615/875 NOK

A smart, contemporary brasserie with a terrace and lovely views
over the water to Aker Brygge; it was once a prison and its name
means 'fortress'. The experienced kitchen create unfussy, attractively
presented modern Nordic dishes using fresh local produce. The
impressive wine list is strong on burgundy.

FJORD ‖○

SEAFOOD • DESIGN • FASHIONABLE

Kristian Augusts gt. 11 ⊠ 0164 **PLAN: C2**
Ⓜ National Theatret
TEL. 22 98 2150 – www.restaurantfjord.no
Closed Christmas, Easter, Sunday and Monday

Menu 445/695 NOK (dinner only) (tasting menu only)
(booking essential)

A contemporary restaurant opposite the National Gallery. Inside
it's dimly lit, with an open kitchen, unusual cobalt blue walls and
buffalo horns set into the chandeliers. The 3-6 course menu offers
flavoursome seafood dishes.

FYR BISTRONOMI & BAR ⭑⚪

MODERN CUISINE • TRENDY • INTIMATE   ♿ 🏠 A/C

Underhaugsveien 28 ✉ 0354 **PLAN: B1**
TEL. 459 16 392 – www.fyrbistronomi.no
Closed Christmas, Easter and Sunday
Menu 350/695 NOK – Carte 360/785 NOK

A vibrant restaurant in the barrel-ceilinged cellar of a striking 19C building; its summer terrace overlooks the adjacent park. Refined modern bistro cooking: smørrebrød and snacks at lunch; creative, generously sized dishes at dinner. Must-tries include the langoustine and oysters.

GRAND CAFÉ ⭑⚪

MODERN CUISINE • CLASSIC DÉCOR • VINTAGE   🍸 🏠 A/C 🔄

Grand H.Oslo by Scandic • Karl Johans Gate 31 ✉ 0159 **PLAN: C2**
Ⓜ Stortinget
TEL. 98 182 000 – www.grandcafeoslo.no
Closed Easter and Christmas
Carte 425/585 NOK

This iconic restaurant dates from 1874; look out for the colourful mural depicting past regulars including Edvard Munch and Henrik Ibsen. The concise menu lists flavour-filled Nordic and international dishes. The cellar wine bar opens Tues-Sat and offers snacks, charcuterie and over 1,500 bottles of wine.

HAPPOLATI ⅈ○

ASIAN • DESIGN • FRIENDLY

St. Olavs Plass 2 ⊠ 0165 **PLAN: C1**
Ⓜ National Theatret
TEL. 479 78 087 – www.happolati.no
Closed Christmas, Easter, Sunday and Monday

Menu 525/750 NOK – Carte 385/425 NOK (dinner only)

This bright, modish restaurant fuses Asian and Nordic styles; its assured cooking uses good quality ingredients and many dishes are designed for sharing. Tightly packed tables and friendly service add to the vibrant ambience.

HOS THEA ⅈ○

ITALIAN • FAMILY • NEIGHBOURHOOD

Gabels gate 11 ⊠ 0272 **PLAN: A2**
TEL. 22 44 68 74 – www.hosthea.no
Closed July, 24-26 December and 18-22 April

Menu 575 NOK – Carte 575/730 NOK (dinner only)

A small, well-established restaurant in a charming residential area. It's decorated in natural hues and hung with beautiful oils. Menus offer a concise selection of Mediterranean dishes; start with the delicious homemade bread.

KOLONIALEN BISLETT ⑩

MODERN CUISINE • BRASSERIE • NEIGHBOURHOOD 🏠 A/C

Sofiesgate 16 ✉ 0170 **PLAN: C1**
TEL. 90 115 098 – www.kolonialenbislett.no
Closed July, Sunday and bank holidays

Carte 540/620 NOK (dinner only and Saturday lunch)
(booking essential)

Close to the stadium you'll find this cosy, modern bistro – previously a grocer's shop for nearly 80 years. The concise, keenly priced menu includes oysters, cured meats and wholesome Norwegian classics that have been brought up-to-date.

LING LING ⑩

CANTONESE • FASHIONABLE   < 🏠 A/C ⟷

Stranden 30 ✉ 0250 **PLAN: B3**
TEL. 24 13 38 00 – www.lingling.hakkasan.com/oslo
Closed 24-27 December, 1 January and Sunday
Menu 298/988 NOK – Carte 325/880 NOK

This more casual sister to Hakkasan offers an abbreviated menu of its signature Cantonese dishes but made using Norwegian produce. It has a great marina location, a cool lounge-bar and a terrific rooftop bar and terrace come summer.

LOFOTEN FISKERESTAURANT ⑪○

SEAFOOD • BRASSERIE • SIMPLE

Stranden 75 ⊠ 0250 PLAN: B3
TEL. 22 83 08 08 – www.lofotenfiskerestaurant.no
Closed Christmas
Menu 395/565 NOK – Carte 455/645 NOK

A traditional fjord-side restaurant hung with bright modern artwork
and offering lovely views from its large windows and sizeable terrace.
Watch as fresh, simply cooked fish and shellfish are prepared in the
semi-open kitchen.

NODEE BARCODE ⑪○

ASIAN • FASHIONABLE • TRENDY

Dronning Eufemais gate 28 ⊠ 0191 PLAN: D3
Ⓜ Jernbanetorget
TEL. 22 93 34 50 – www.nodee.no
Closed 24 December-1 January, 18-22 April, Sunday and bank
holidays
Menu 335/658 NOK – Carte 310/970 NOK

A moody, elegant restaurant serving an all-encompassing Asian menu
featuring dim sum, sushi and dishes cooked on the Robata grill –
crispy Peking duck is their speciality. There's a bar and terrace on
the 13th floor and on the 14th floor is Nodee Sky, with its appealing
set menu and city views.

OMAKASE BY VLADIMIR PAK 🍴○

SUSHI • DESIGN

Ruseløkkveien 3, 1st floor ⊠ 0251 **PLAN: B2**
TEL. 456 85 022 – www.omakaseoslo.no
Closed Christmas, Easter, Sunday and bank holidays
Menu 1350 NOK (dinner only)

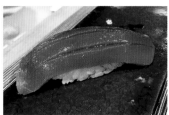

This restaurant comprises a three-sided counter with seats for 15.
The fish and shellfish come largely from Norwegian waters and the
rice is American. The no-choice menu offers around 18 servings of
Edomae-style sushi, although there can be surprises, like reindeer;
some wine pairings are equally original.

PLAH 🍴○

THAI • NEIGHBOURHOOD • FRIENDLY

Hegdehaugsveien 22 ⊠ 0167 **PLAN: B1**
TEL. 22 56 43 00 – www.plah.no
Closed 2 weeks July, Christmas, Easter and Sunday-Monday
Menu 595/845 NOK – Carte 735/845 NOK (dinner only)

Norwegian ingredients blend with Thai flavours at this well-
run restaurant. Choose between the à la carte and 2 tasting
menus: 'Journey Through Thailand' or 'Journey Through The Jungle'
(vegetarian). Dishes are eye-catching, imaginative and full of flavour.
Their neighbouring bar serves Thai street food.

RESTAURANTEIK ⅼㆁ

MODERN CUISINE • FRIENDLY • MINIMALIST   Ⓐ/Ⓒ ⇌

Clarion Collection H. Savoy, Universitetsgata 11 ⊠ 0164 **PLAN: C2**
Ⓜ National Theatret
TEL. 22 36 07 10 – www.restauranteik.no
Closed July, Easter, Christmas, Sunday and Monday
Menu 395 NOK (dinner only) (tasting menu only)

Colourful abstract screens adorn the walls of this hotel restaurant close to the National Gallery. There's an inventive European element to the cooking, which is also informed by the chef's travels. The wine list offers a good range of older vintages, especially from Burgundy and Bordeaux.

STATHOLDERENS
MAT OG VIN KJELLER ⅼㆁ

NORWEGIAN • RUSTIC • SIMPLE

Statholdergaarden • Rådhusgate 11 (entrance from
Kirkegata) ⊠ 0151 Ⓜ Stortinget **PLAN: C3**
TEL. 22 41 88 00 – www.statholdergaarden.no
Closed July, 22 December-3 January, Sunday and bank holidays
Menu 750 NOK – Carte 750/980 NOK (dinner only) (booking essential)

The informal sister of Statholdergaarden – set over three rooms in the old vaults beneath it. One wall of the large entranceway is filled with wine bottles. Choose from a huge array of small plates or go for the 10 course tasting menu.

THEATERCAFÉEN ⏐○

TRADITIONAL CUISINE • LUXURY •
ROMANTIC

Continental Hotel • Stortingsgaten 24-26 ✉ 0117 PLAN: C2
Ⓜ National Theatret
TEL. 22 82 40 50 – www.theatercafeen.no
Closed 4 weeks July-August and Easter
Menu 655 NOK (dinner) – Carte 550/950 NOK

A truly grand café, with tiled flooring, art deco lights, pillars and a
vaulted ceiling; it's been a meeting point for the good and the great of
the Norwegian cultural scene since 1900. Lunch offers lighter dishes,
sandwiches, pastries and cakes; dinner is the time for more classic
dishes.

TJUVHOLMEN SJØMAGASINET ⏐○

SEAFOOD • FASHIONABLE • BRASSERIE

Tjuvholmen Allé 14 ✉ 0252 PLAN: B3
TEL. 23 89 77 77 – www.sjomagasinet.no
Closed Christmas, Easter, Sunday and bank holidays
Menu 355/685 NOK – Carte 600/775 NOK

A vast restaurant with three dining rooms, a crab and lobster tank,
a superb terrace and a wet fish shop. Its name means 'sea store' and
menus are fittingly seafood based. Shellfish is from the nearby dock
– the langoustines are fantastic.

VAAGHALS 🍴⚪

SCANDINAVIAN • BRASSERIE • FASHIONABLE   ♿ 🏠 [AC] 🍽

Dronning Eufemias gate 8 ✉ 0151 **PLAN: D3**
Ⓜ Jernbanetorget
TEL. 920 70 999 – www.vaaghals.com
Closed last 3 weeks July, 22 December-3 January, Easter and
Sunday

Menu 715 NOK (dinner) – Carte 475/815 NOK

A bright, contemporary restaurant with an open kitchen and a terrace;
located on the ground floor of one of the modern 'barcode' buildings.
Scandinavian menus feature dry-aged meat; many of the dinner
dishes are designed for sharing.

CONTINENTAL   🏰

GRAND LUXURY • TRADITIONAL • CLASSIC
🌿 ♿ 💆 [AC] 🧖 🚗

Stortingsgaten 24-26 ✉ 0117 Ⓜ National Theatret **PLAN: C2**
TEL. 22 82 40 00 – www.hotelcontinental.no
Closed Christmas-New Year

155 rm 🛏 – ♦ 3505/5595 NOK ♦♦ 3505/5595 NOK – 2 suites
THEATERCAFÉEN – See restaurant listing

A classic hotel situated by the National Theatre and run by the 4th
generation of the family, who ensure the service remains personal.
Bedrooms are stylish and contemporary – the corner suites have
balconies and views of the Royal Palace. Dine in the grand café or
from an inventive daily menu in Annen Etage.

GRAND H.OSLO BY SCANDIC

GRAND LUXURY • HISTORIC • ELEGANT

Karl Johans Gate 31 ✉ 0159 **PLAN: C2**
Ⓜ Stortinget
TEL. 23 21 20 00 - www.grand.no
274 rm ☕ - 🚹 2180/4810 NOK 👥 3490/5090 NOK - 5 suites
GRAND CAFÉ - See restaurant listing

An imposing, centrally located hotel built in 1874; the guest areas and grand ballrooms reflect this. Bedrooms are charming: some are modern, some are feminine and others are in a belle époque style. Dine on international fare in elegant Palmen or Nordic-inspired cooking in the Grand Café.

CLARION COLLECTION H. BASTION

BUSINESS • MODERN • PERSONALISED

Skippergata 5-7 ✉ 0152 **PLAN: C3**
Ⓜ Jernbanetorget
TEL. 22 47 77 00 - www.nordicchoicehotels.no
Closed 20 December-1 January and 12-23 April
99 rm ☕ - 🚹 840/2935 NOK 👥 990/3235 NOK - 5 suites

Two unassuming buildings house this boutique business hotel. The lounge has an English country house feel and an unusual collection of pictures and antiques are displayed throughout. Go for one of the newer, more characterful bedrooms. The small restaurant offers a complimentary one course supper.

CLARION COLLECTION H. GABELSHUS

TRADITIONAL • BUSINESS • CLASSIC

Gabelsgate 16 ✉ 0272 **PLAN: A2**
TEL. 23 27 65 00 – www.nordicchoicehotels.no
Closed Easter and Christmas-New Year
114 rm ☕ – 👤 1180/3000 NOK 👥 1380/3200 NOK – 1 suite

A beautiful ivy-covered house with a classic wood-furnished lounge and a peaceful atmosphere, located in a smart residential neighbourhood. Charming bedrooms are a pleasing mix of traditional and designer styles. Complimentary supper in the evening.

COMFORT H. GRAND CENTRAL

CHAIN • BUSINESS • PERSONALISED

Jernbanetorget 1 ✉ 0154 **PLAN: D2**
Ⓜ Jernbanetorget
TEL. 22 98 28 00 – www.choicehotels.no
170 rm ☕ – 👤 1054/2871 NOK 👥 1054/2871 NOK

A great choice for businesspeople, this delightful hotel has a superb location above the main train station. Many of the soundproofed bedrooms have been individually styled and boast coordinating fabrics and colour schemes, as well as feature bathrooms. The restaurant offers a menu of simple Italian dishes.

OPERA

BUSINESS • MODERN • PERSONALISED

Dronning Eufemias gate 4 ⊠ 0191 **PLAN: D2**
Ⓜ Jernbanetorget
TEL. 24 10 30 00 – www.thonhotels.no/opera
Closed Christmas and New Year
480 rm 🛏 – 🛉 1145/2705 NOK 🛉🛉 1395/3055 NOK – 2 suites

Set on the doorstep of the National Library and the Opera House, this imposing hotel has a subtle theatrical theme both in its décor and the naming of its rooms. Bedrooms come in warm colours; ask for one at the front with a balcony. The Scala restaurant uses Norwegian produce in international recipes.

ROSENKRANTZ

BUSINESS • CHAIN • PERSONALISED

Rosenkrantz gate 1 ⊠ 0159 **PLAN: C2**
Ⓜ National Theatret
TEL. 23 31 55 00 – www.thonhotels.no
151 rm 🛏 – 🛉 1750/3195 NOK 🛉🛉 1750/3495 NOK – 8 suites
BRASSERIE PALEO – See restaurant listing

Located in the city centre and perfect for the business traveller. The brightly styled 8th floor guest lounge has complimentary drinks, snacks and light meals. Functional bedrooms come with Smart TVs and modern bathrooms.

THIEF

LUXURY • CONTEMPORARY • THEMED

Landgangen 1 ✉ 0252 **PLAN: B3**
TEL. 24 00 40 00 – www.thethief.com
116 rm ☕ – ♦ 3000/5000 NOK ♦♦ 3300/5500 NOK – 9 suites

A smart hotel with a superb spa, located on a huge development on Thief Island. Works from global artists – including Andy Warhol – feature throughout. Facilities are state-of-the-art and a tablet controls all of the technology in the bedrooms. Dine on international dishes in Foodbar, which moves to the rooftop in summer.

PARK INN

BUSINESS • CHAIN • MINIMALIST

Ovre Slottsgate 2c ✉ 0157 **PLAN: C2**
Ⓜ Stortinget
TEL. 22 40 01 00 – www.parkinn.com/hotel-oslo
118 rm ☕ – ♦ 995/3295 NOK ♦♦ 1095/3395 NOK

A converted apartment block near Karl Johans Gate. Inside it's bright and modern with pleasant guest areas. Good-sized, functional bedrooms have pale wood furniture and modern lighting; the top floor rooms have balconies.

SAGA H. OSLO

TOWNHOUSE • HISTORIC • PERSONALISED

Eilert Sundstgate 39 ✉ 0259 PLAN: B1
TEL. 22 55 44 90 – www.sagahoteloslo.no
Closed Christmas and Easter
47 rm ☕ – ♦ 995/2895 NOK ♦♦ 1095/3495 NOK

A late Victorian townhouse with a smart, contemporary interior, set in a quiet city suburb. Most of the bedrooms are spacious: they have bold feature walls, modern facilities – including coffee machines – and small but stylish shower rooms. There's a Japanese restaurant in the basement.

SCANDIC VULKAN

BUSINESS • CHAIN • DESIGN

Maridalsveien 13 ✉ 0178 PLAN: D1
TEL. 21 05 71 00 – www.scandichotels.com/vulkan
Closed Christmas and Easter
149 rm ☕ – ♦ 800/2500 NOK ♦♦ 990/3500 NOK

A designer hotel set on the site of a former silver mine, next to a great food market. Modern bedrooms have bold feature walls and good facilities; the external-facing rooms have full-length windows. The bright, semi industrial style restaurant offers Italian-inspired dishes – in summer they only serve pizza.

SPECTRUM

BUSINESS • CHAIN • PERSONALISED

&

Brugata 7 ⊠ 0186 PLAN: D2
Ⓜ Grønland
TEL. 23 36 27 00 – www.thonhotels.no/spectrum
Closed Christmas
187 rm ⬚ – ♦ 1055/2095 NOK ♦♦ 1750/2695 NOK

This unassuming looking hotel sits on a pedestrianised shopping street, not far from the station. Bright, bold colours feature in a funky interior with all the facilities a modern traveller needs; go for a larger Business Room.

VIKA ATRIUM

BUSINESS • CHAIN • FUNCTIONAL

Munkedamsveien 45 ⊠ 0250 PLAN: B2
Ⓜ National Theatret
TEL. 22 83 33 00 – www.thonhotels.no
103 rm ⬚ – ♦ 995/1995 NOK ♦♦ 1195/2395 NOK

This busy business hotel is just minutes from Aker Brygge's harbourside shops and restaurants, in a block containing a large conference centre; some of the contemporary bedrooms overlook the atrium. Breakfasts feature organic produce.

LYSVERKET

MODERN CUISINE • DESIGN • FASHIONABLE

Rasmus Meyers Allé 9 ⊠ 5015
TEL. 55 60 3100 – www.lysverket.no
Closed 23 December-3 January, 1 week Easter, Sunday and Monday
Menu 999 NOK – Carte 570/1050 NOK (dinner only)

Large, stylish restaurant located in a 1930s art museum overlooking a park and lake. The modern dishes come with a pleasing simplicity, with the focus on fish and seafood; sharing is encouraged. The young team provides warm and engaging service.

RE-NAA ✿

CREATIVE • INTIMATE • ELEGANT

Steinkargata 10 (Breitorget) ⊠ 4006
TEL. 51 55 11 11 – www.restaurantrenaa.no
Closed mid July-mid August, Christmas-New Year, Easter and Sunday-Tuesday
Menu 1600 NOK (dinner only)
(tasting menu only) (booking essential)

Chef:
Sven Erik Renaa

Specialities:
Cod with shore crab and lemon verbena. Summer lamb with fava beans and cucumber. 'Egg and Toast'.

An elegant restaurant run by the talented Sven Erik Renaa; moving in February 2019 to a new site nearby. The set seasonal menu utilises exceptionally fresh, first class ingredients to produce complex dishes with an impressive balance, a wonderful purity and a superb depth of flavour. Seafood is a highlight.

SABI OMAKASE ✿

SUSHI • INTIMATE • FRIENDLY

Pedersgata 38 ✉ 4013
TEL. 925 43 781 – www.omakase.no
Closed Christmas, July and Sunday-Wednesday

Menu 1495 NOK (dinner only) (tasting menu only)
(booking essential)

Chef:
Roger Asakil Joya
Specialities:
Sashimi. 17 courses of nigiri.
Seasonal ice cream.

Sit at one of the ten seats at the counter to enjoy a multi-course sushi experience, with each course introduced and explained by the experienced chef-owner. Superlative Norwegian ingredients are prepared with exceptional skill and embellished with subtle modern touches. Sake or wine pairings accompany.

TANGO ⑩

MODERN CUISINE • INTIMATE • DESIGN

Skagen 3 ✉ 4006
TEL. 51 50 12 30 – www.tango-bk.no
Closed Christmas, Easter, Sunday-Monday and bank holidays

Menu 1490 NOK (dinner only and Saturday lunch)
(tasting menu only) (booking essential)

The move from the harbour to these premises in 2018 worked well. This intimate little restaurant, with striking modern artwork, comes with just nine tables. The visually appealing dishes offer clear flavours, freshness and creativity; they also come paired with well-chosen wine flights.

CREDO ✿

CREATIVE • DESIGN • NEIGHBOURHOOD   ♿

Ladeveien 9 (Northeast: 2.5 km by Innherredsveien, Mellomveien and Jarleveien off Stjødalsveien) ✉ 7066
TEL. 954 37 028 – www.restaurantcredo.no
Closed 2 weeks July-August, Christmas, Sunday-Tuesday and bank holidays

Menu 1300 NOK (dinner only) (tasting menu only)
(booking essential)

Chef:
Heidi Bjerkan

Specialities:
King crab. Duck with plums from Klakken. Fresh milk ice cream, caramel, laurel oil and coffee crumble.

An airy restaurant with an up-to-date urban feel, set in a striking former factory. Championing the produce of the Trøndelag region and supporting local farms and artisan producers is key to the ingredient-led 20-26 course surprise menu. Cooking is highly creative yet understated; natural in style with a delicate balance.

FAGN ✿

MODERN CUISINE • INTIMATE • CONTEMPORARY DÉCOR

Ørjaveita 4 (Ground floor restaurant) ✉ 7010
TEL. 458 44 996 – www.fagn.no
Closed 8 July-1 August, 23 December-3 January, Easter, Sunday and Monday

Menu 750 NOK (weekdays)/1385 NOK (dinner only)
(tasting menu only) (booking essential)

Chef:
Jonas Andre Nåvik

Specialities:
Turbot, mussels and green apples. Duck, chanterelles and celeriac. Meadowsweet, oats and brown butter.

This intimate ground floor restaurant has a back-to-nature feel and serves 5, 10 and 20 course menus which evolve with the seasons. Childhood memories inspire many of the flavour-packed dishes, which ally modern techniques to traditional principles – and are finished off at the table with a flamboyant flourish.

Dougall_Photography/iStock

SWEDEN

STARS & BIB GOURMAND

STOCKHOLM

Sweden

mikdam/iStock

Stockholm is the place to go for clean air, big skies and handsome architecture. And water. One of the great beauties of the city is the amount of water that runs through and around it; it's built on 14 islands, and looks out on 24,000 of them. An astounding two-thirds of the area within the city limits is made up of water, parks and woodland, and there are dozens of little bridges to cross to get from one part of town to another. It's little wonder Swedes appear so calm and relaxed. It's in Stockholm that the salty waters of the Baltic meet head-on the fresh waters of Lake Mälaren, reflecting the broad boulevards and

elegant buildings that shimmer along their edge. Domes, spires and turrets dot a skyline that in the summertime never truly darkens. The heart of the city is the Old Town, Gamla Stan, full of alleyways and lanes little changed from their medieval origins. Just to the north is the modern centre, Norrmalm: a buzzing quarter of shopping malls, restaurants and bars. East of Gamla Stan you reach the small island of Skeppsholmen, which boasts fine views of the waterfront; directly north from here is Östermalm, an area full of grand residences, while southeast you'll find the lovely park island of Djurgården. South and west of Gamla Stan are the two areas where Stockholmers particularly like to hang out, the trendy (and hilly) Södermalm, and Kungsholmen.

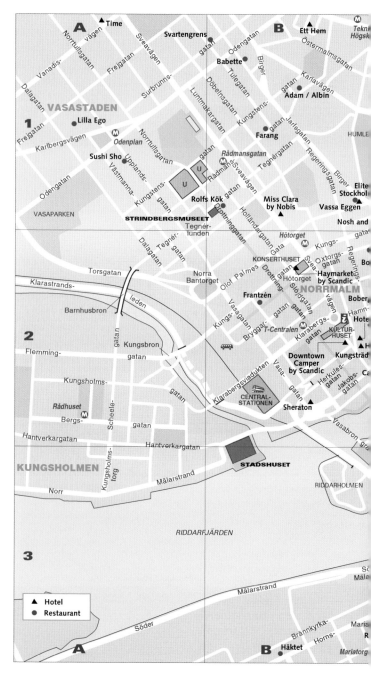

A

▲Time

Svartengrens
gatan

Odengatan

B

▲Ett Hem

Tekni
Högsk

Östermalmsgatan

Babette●

Birger

Tulegatan

Karlavägen

Döbelnsgatan

gatan Jarlsgatan

●Adam / Albin

HUMLE

VASASTADEN

●Lilla Ego

Ⓜ
Odenplan

Surbrunns-

Lummakrgatan

Kungstens-

gatan

Farang●

Sushi Sho●

Uplands-

Norrullsgatan

gatan

Rådmansgatan

Tegnérgatan

Ⓜ
Rådmans-
Sveavägen

Regeringsgatan

Birger

Elite
Stockhol ▲

Rolfs Kök●

Drottninggatan

Hölländargatan

Miss Clara
by Nobis ▲

Vassa Eggen●

STRINDBERGSMUSEET

Tegnér-
lunden

Hötorget Ⓜ

Nosh and

gata

Dalagatan

Tegnér-
gatan

Norra
Bantorget

Olof Palmes

Drottninggatan

KONSERTHUSET
Hötorget

Kungs-

Sveavägen

Oxtorgs-
gatan

Regerings-

Bo

Haymarket
by Scandic

gatan

Torsgatan

Klarastrands-

leden

Frantzén●

NORRMALM

Bober●

Hamn-

Barnhusbron

gatan

T-Centralen Ⓜ

Bryggar-

gatan

Klaraberg-
gatan

Hote

▲H

Kungsbron

Flemming-

gatan

🚍

Downtown
Camper
by Scandic

Vasa-

Kungsträd

Herkules-
gatan

Jakobs-
gatan

Ca

Kungsholms-

Klarabergsviadukten

gatan

🚂

**CENTRAL-
STATIONEN**

Sheraton ▲

Rådhuset

Ⓜ

Bergs-

Scheele-

gatan

Vasabron gra

Hantverkargatan

Hantverkargatan

KUNGSHOLMEN

Kungsholms-
torg

Mälarstrand

STADSHUSET

RIDDARHOLMEN

Norr

RIDDARFJÄRDEN

Så
Mäla

▲	Hotel
●	Restaurant

Mälarstrand

Söder

Brännkyrka-

Horns-

Maria

R

A

B ●Häktet

Mariatorg

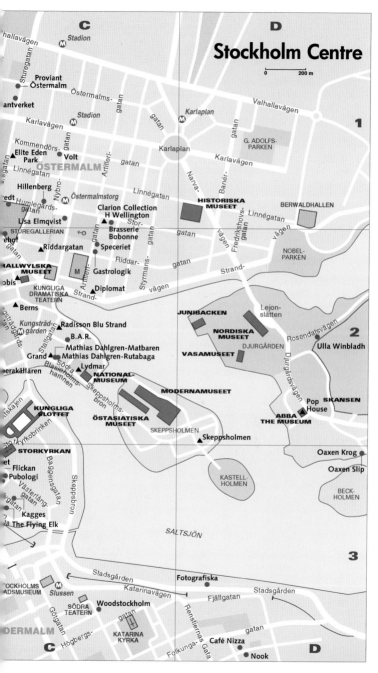

FRANTZÉN ✿✿✿

MODERN CUISINE • DESIGN • FASHIONABLE   A/C

Klara Norra Kyrkogata 26 ✉ 111 22 PLAN: B2
Ⓜ T-Centralen
TEL. 08-20 85 80 – www.restaurantfrantzen.com
Closed 16 June-18 July, 23 December-10 January and Sunday-Tuesday
Menu 3200 SEK (tasting menu only) (booking essential)

Chef:
Björn Frantzén

Specialities:
Langoustine with Koshihikari rice, onions and ginger butter emulsion. Guinea fowl with blond miso, vin jaune, walnuts and smoked morels. Tea, milk and honey.

A unique restaurant set over 3 floors of a 19C property; ring the doorbell, enjoy an aperitif in the living room and have the day's luxurious ingredients explained. A beautiful wood counter borders the sleek kitchen and the chefs present, finish and explain the flavour-packed meals personally. Cooking is modern and creative but also uses classic techniques.

GASTROLOGIK ✿✿

CREATIVE • MINIMALIST • DESIGN   🐌

Artillerigatan 14 ✉ 114 51 PLAN: C2
Ⓜ Östermalmstorg
TEL. 08-662 30 60 – www.gastrologik.se
Closed Christmas-New Year, midsummer, Sunday and Monday
Menu 1595 SEK (dinner only) (surprise menu only)
(booking essential)

Chef:
Jacob Holmström and Anton Bjuhr

Specialities:
Shrimps with horseradish, dill and shrimp pancake. Quail with peas, hay broth and quail fat. Yoghurt curd, frozen gooseberries and lilac infusion.

Everything starts with the ingredients for the two chef-owners; they met as apprentices – one is from the north, the other the south – so both bring something different. The day's produce decides the Surprise menu – 20 or so beautiful dishes that are creative in their contrasts of flavour and texture.

AGRIKULTUR ✿

MODERN CUISINE • COSY • NEIGHBOURHOOD

Roslagsgatan 43
(Northwest: 2.5 km by Birger Jarlsgatan) ✉ 113 54
TEL. 08-15 02 02 – www.agrikultur.se
Closed 1 June-16 August, Christmas, Easter and Sunday-Monday
Menu 945 SEK (dinner only) (tasting menu only)
(booking essential)

Chef:
Filip Fastén

Specialities:
Jerusalem artichoke, green pepper
and sesame seeds. Cabbage, whey,
mushroom and red deer. Cherries,
long pepper and lemon thyme.

A lovely little restaurant with a certain homespun charm. The passionate young team deliver a multi-course menu which follows a local, seasonal and sustainable ethos. Creative cooking sees modernised Swedish classics prepared using some more traditional methods, and the Aga and wood-burning oven play a key part.

EKSTEDT ✿

MEATS AND GRILLS • DESIGN • FRIENDLY   ✿ &

Humlegårdsgatan 17 ✉ 11446 **PLAN: C1**
Ⓜ Östermalmstorg
TEL. 08-611 12 10 – www.ekstedt.nu
Closed Christmas, New Year, midsummer, Sunday and Monday
Menu 890/1250 SEK (dinner only) (tasting menu only)
(booking essential)

Chef:
Niklas Ekstedt

Specialities:
Dried deer, leek, bleak roe and
charcoal cream. Wild duck roasted
over birch with forest mushrooms,
capers and lovage. Wood oven-
baked almond cake, blueberries
and apple.

An unassuming façade hides a very relaxed, friendly, yet professionally run brasserie, where ingredients are cooked in a wood-burning oven, over a fire-pit or smoked through a chimney using birch wood. Dishes are inventive but well-balanced – they are given their finishing touches at the stone bar.

MATHIAS DAHLGREN-MATBAREN ✿

MODERN CUISINE • FASHIONABLE • DESIGN   ♿ A/C

Grand Hotel • Södra Blasieholmshamnen 6 ⊠ 103 27 PLAN: C2
Ⓜ Kungsträdgården
TEL. 08-679 35 84 – www.mdghs.com
Closed 12 July-5 August, 22 December-6 January, Saturday lunch, bank holiday lunch and Sunday
Carte 465/1275 SEK

Specialities:
Langoustine from Bohuslän. Roe deer and wild mushrooms. Baked white chocolate, toffee, sour cream and nuts.

This popular hotel restaurant is both fun and charmingly run. The open kitchen specialises in flavoursome, well-balanced dishes from an appealing menu divided into the headings 'From our country', 'From other countries' and 'From the plant world'. They keep some seats at the counter for those who haven't booked.

OPERAKÄLLAREN ✿

CLASSIC CUISINE • LUXURY • HISTORIC   ✿ ⊡

Operahuset, Karl XII's Torg ⊠ 111 86 PLAN: C2
Ⓜ Kungsträdgården
TEL. 08-676 58 01 – www.operakallaren.se
Closed 1 December-15 January, July, midsummer, Sunday and Monday
Menu 1050/1550 SEK (dinner only)

Specialities:
Tartare of beef with beetroot and quail's egg. Saddle of roe deer with cabbage, game jus and cranberries. Prunes flambé in rum.

Sweden's most opulent restaurant sits within the historic Opera House, and the stunning, high-ceilinged room boasts original gilt panelling decorated with frescoes and carvings. Carefully constructed dishes are underpinned by classic techniques. The wine list boasts extensive vintages of the world's great wines.

SUSHI SHO ✿

JAPANESE • NEIGHBOURHOOD • FRIENDLY

Upplandsgatan 45 ✉ 113 28 **PLAN: A1**
Ⓜ Odenplan
TEL. 08-30 30 30 – www.sushisho.se
Closed July, Christmas, New Year, midsummer, Sunday and Monday

Menu 685 SEK (dinner only and Saturday lunch) (surprise menu only) (booking essential)

Chef:
Carl Ishizaki

Specialities:
Mackerel saba-bosushi with white kombu and sesame. Soy-cured egg yolk with char, okra and roasted rice.

With its white tiled walls and compact counter seating, the room couldn't be simpler; the food, by contrast, is sublime. Meals are served omakase-style, with the chef deciding what's best each day and dishes arriving as they're ready. Top quality seafood from local waters features alongside some great egg recipes.

VOLT ✿

CREATIVE • INTIMATE • NEIGHBOURHOOD

Kommendörsgatan 16 ✉ 114 48 **PLAN: C1**
Ⓜ Stadion
TEL. 08-662 34 00 – www.restaurangvolt.se
Closed 15 July-11 August, Christmas, New Year and Sunday-Monday

Menu 750/950 SEK (dinner only and Saturday lunch)
(booking essential)

Chef:
Peter Andersson and Fredrik Johnsson

Specialities:
Lettuce, chicken and beach rose. Lamb, onion and sourdough. Plum with fennel and cream.

An intimate, welcoming restaurant run by a young but experienced team. Cooking is natural in style, with the largely organic produce yielding clear, bold flavours – natural wines also feature. Ingredients are arranged in layers, so that each forkful contains a little of everything; choose 4 or 6 courses.

BRASSERIE BOBONNE 👻

FRENCH • COSY • BISTRO

Storgatan 12 ✉ 114 51 PLAN: C1
Ⓜ Östermalmstorg
TEL. 08-660 03 18 – www.bobonne.se
Closed 4 weeks summer, Easter, Christmas, Saturday lunch and Sunday
Menu 550 SEK (dinner) – Carte 345/650 SEK

This sweet neighbourhood restaurant has a warm, homely feel, and the owners proudly welcome their guests from the open kitchen. Modern artwork hangs on the walls and contrasts with traditional features such as mosaic tiling. Classic cooking has a French core and dishes show obvious care in their preparation.

LILLA EGO 👻

MODERN CUISINE • BISTRO • FRIENDLY   ⟠

Västmannag 69 ✉ 113 26 PLAN: A1
Ⓜ Odenplan
TEL. 08-27 44 55 – www.lillaego.com
Closed July, Christmas, New Year, Easter, midsummer, Sunday and Monday
Carte 465/675 SEK (dinner only) (booking essential)

Still one of the hottest tickets in town, Lilla Ego comes with a pared-down look and a buzzy vibe; if you haven't booked, try for a counter seat. The two modest chef-owners have created an appealingly priced menu of robust seasonal dishes. The 'wrestling' sausage will challenge even the biggest of appetites.

PROVIANT ÖSTERMALM

SWEDISH • BISTRO • INTIMATE

Sturegatan 19 ✉ 11436 **PLAN: C1**
Ⓜ Stadion
TEL. 08-22 60 50 - www.proviant.se
Closed 3 weeks July, 2 weeks Christmas, Saturday lunch and Sunday

Menu 295/425 SEK - Carte 440/585 SEK

Behind an inconspicuous façade in a chic residential area lies this lively restaurant which mixes Swedish and French charm. Choose from rustic, classically based dishes on the blackboard, a French-inspired à la carte or the house specialities. Many of the wines are available by the glass.

ROLFS KÖK

MODERN CUISINE • BISTRO • RUSTIC

Tegnérgatan 41 ✉ 111 61 **PLAN: B1**
Ⓜ Rådmansgatan
TEL. 08-10 16 96 - www.rolfskok.se
Closed 21-23 June, 8 July-4 August, 24-25 December, 31 December-6 January and lunch Saturday-Sunday

Menu 165 SEK (lunch) - Carte dinner 415/695 SEK (booking essential)

A buzzing neighbourhood restaurant in a lively commercial district, run by a passionate chef-owner. The contemporary interior was designed by famous Swedish artists; sit at the counter to watch the chefs in action. Dishes include homely classics and blackboard specials - every dish has a wine match.

ADAM / ALBIN 🍴

MODERN CUISINE • INTIMATE • NEIGHBOURHOOD ♿ 🄰🄲

Rådmansgatan 16 ✉ 114 25 **PLAN: B1**
Ⓜ Tekniska Högskolan
TEL. 08-411 55 35 – www.adamalbin.se
Closed Christmas, Sunday, bank holidays and restricted opening in summer
Menu 895/1595 SEK (dinner only) (booking essential)

Owners Adam and Albin have stamped their mark on this charming restaurant, which comes with Italian marble clad walls and a mix of individual and communal tables. Snacks are followed by a 5 or 10 course menu, where refined, eye-catching dishes blend the ethos of a Scandic kitchen with Asian flavours.

AG 🍴

MEATS AND GRILLS • RUSTIC • FASHIONABLE 🌐 🄰🄲

Kronobergsgatan 37 (2nd Floor), Kungsholmen
(via Flemminggatan) ✉ 112 33
Ⓜ Fridshemsplan
TEL. 08-410 68 100 – www.restaurangag.se
Closed 6 July-5 August, 24-25 December, 30 December-6 January and Sunday
Carte 345/935 SEK (dinner only)

An industrial, New York style eatery on the 2nd floor of an old silver factory. Swedish, American and Scottish beef is displayed in huge cabinets and you choose your accompaniments. Expect a great wine list and smooth service.

BABETTE ⠑⃝

MODERN CUISINE • NEIGHBOURHOOD • BISTRO

Roslagsgatan 6 ⊠ 113 55 PLAN: B1
Ⓜ Tekniska Högskolan
TEL. 08-509 022 24 – www.babette.se
Closed 23-25 and 31 December, 1 January and 17-24 June
Carte 185/545 SEK (dinner only)

You'll feel at home in this modern neighbourhood bistro. Cooking is rustic and unfussy and the daily selection of small plates and pizzas makes dining flexible. They limit their bookings so that they can accommodate walk-ins.

B.A.R. ⠑⃝

SEAFOOD • BRASSERIE • FASHIONABLE   AC

Blasieholmsgatan 4a ⊠ 111 48 PLAN: C2
Ⓜ Kungsträdgården
TEL. 08-611 53 35 – www.restaurangbar.se
Closed Christmas-New Year, Saturday lunch and Sunday
Carte 345/595 SEK

This bright, buzzy restaurant is just a cast away from the waterfront and has a semi-industrial fish-market style. Choose your seafood from the fridge or the tank, along with a cooking style, a sauce and one of their interesting sides.

BOBERGS 🍴

SPANISH • TAPAS BAR • FASHIONABLE   ♿ 🅰🅲

MODERN CUISINE • ELEGANT • CLASSIC DÉCOR   ♿ 🅰🅲

NK Department Store (4th floor),
Hamngatan 18-20 ✉ 111 47 **PLAN: B2**
Ⓜ Kungsträdgården
TEL. 08-762 81 61 – www.bobergsmatsal.se
Closed 16 July-13 August, Christmas, Sunday and bank holidays
Menu 395 SEK – Carte 419/655 SEK (lunch only)

Head past the canteen in this historic department store to the elegant
birch-panelled room and ask for a river view. Choose the set business
lunch or from the seasonal à la carte; classic cooking mixes French
and Swedish influences.

BOQUERIA 🍴

SPANISH • TAPAS BAR • FASHIONABLE   ♿ 🏠

Jakobsbergsgatan 17 ✉ 111 44 **PLAN: B2**
Ⓜ Hötorget
TEL. 08-30 74 00 – www.boqueria.se
Closed 24-25 December, 1 January and midsummer
Carte 300/450 SEK

A vibrant, bustling tapas restaurant with high-level seating, located
in a smart mall. Appealing menus offer tapas and a range of authentic
dishes for two or more to share. Sangria and pintxos can be enjoyed
in their nearby bar.

CAROUSEL ᵀⓘO

SWEDISH • CLASSIC DÉCOR • HISTORIC   🦽 🛜 Ⓐ⒞

Gustav Adolfs Torg 20 ✉ 111 53 **PLAN: B2**
Ⓜ Kungsträdgården
TEL. 08-10 27 57 – www.restaurantcarousel.se
Closed Christmas, New Year, midsummer and Sunday

Carte 295/765 SEK

Enjoy a drink under the impressive original ceiling in the bar before taking a seat near the carousel or out on the terrace. The experienced chefs carefully prepare flavoursome dishes which follow the seasons and have classic Swedish roots.

FARANG ᵀⓘO

SOUTH EAST ASIAN • MINIMALIST • FASHIONABLE   🦽 Ⓐ⒞

Tulegatan 7 ✉ 113 53 **PLAN: B1**
Ⓜ Rådmansgatan
TEL. 08-673 74 00 – www.farang.se
Closed July and Sunday-Monday

Menu 285/575 SEK (lunch) – Carte dinner 410/640 SEK

The unusual front door harks back to its Stockholm Electric Company days, and behind it lies a stylish restaurant and bar – the former sits in the old machine hall. Zingy, aromatic dishes focus on Southeast Asia and are full of colour.

HANTVERKET 🍴

MODERN CUISINE • RUSTIC • FASHIONABLE

Sturegatan 15 ✉ 114 36 PLAN: C1
Ⓜ Stadion
TEL. 08-121 321 60 – www.restauranghantverket.se
Closed July, Christmas, New Year, Easter, Saturday lunch and
Sunday

Menu 295 SEK (weekday lunch) – Carte 295/460 SEK

Exposed ducting contrasts with chunky tables and leafy plants at this
buzzy restaurant. It has a cool lounge-bar, counter seats and a mix
of raised and regular tables. Cooking has an artisanal Swedish heart
and service is bright and breezy.

HILLENBERG 🍴

MODERN CUISINE • DESIGN • BRASSERIE

Humlegårdsgatan 14 ✉ 114 34 PLAN: C1
Ⓜ Östermalmstorg
TEL. 08-519 421 53 – www.hillenberg.se
Closed 24 December, 1 January, Sunday and lunch mid July-mid
August

Carte 425/840 SEK (booking essential at lunch)

Perfectly pitched for busy Humlegårdsgatan is this stylish take on a
classic brasserie. It has a smart, elegant feel and a hugely impressive
wine cellar. Appealing Swedish classics are immensely satisfying yet
exhibit a subtle modern touch and sense of finesse.

LISA ELMQVIST 🍴◯

SEAFOOD • FAMILY • BISTRO

Humlesgårdsgatan 1 ✉ 114 39 PLAN: C1
◎ Östermalmstorg
TEL. 08-553 40 4 10 – www.lisaelmqvist.se
Closed 24 December, midsummer, Sunday and bank holidays
Carte 503/960 SEK (booking essential at lunch)

While the original 19C market hall is being restored, this established family-run restaurant is operating from the temporary marketplace next door. Top quality seafood from the day's catch features in unfussy, satisfying combinations.

MATHIAS DAHLGREN-RUTABAGA 🍴◯

VEGETARIAN • SIMPLE • FASHIONABLE   ⚜ ♿ 🄰🄲

Grand Hotel • Södra Blasieholmshamnen 6 ✉ 103 27 PLAN: C2
◎ Kungsträdgården
TEL. 08-679 35 84 – www.mdghs.se
Closed 22 December-6 January, 12 July-5 August, Sunday and Monday
Menu 495/795 SEK (dinner only) (tasting menu only)
(booking essential)

A light, bright restaurant offering something one doesn't usually find in grand hotels – vegetarian cuisine. The two set menus come with flavours from across the globe; choose the chef's table for a more personal experience.

NOSH AND CHOW ⊩○

INTERNATIONAL • BRASSERIE • FASHIONABLE ⅙ Ⓐ/C ⇔

Norrlandsgatan 24 ⊠ 111 43 **PLAN: B2**
Ⓜ Hötorget
TEL. 08-503 389 60 – www.noshandchow.se
Closed Easter, 24 December, 1 January, midsummer, Saturday lunch and Sunday
Menu 315 SEK (lunch) – Carte 300/725 SEK

This former bank has been transformed into a glitzy cocktail bar and brasserie which displays a smart mix of New York and New England styling. Filling dishes blend French, American and Swedish influences with other global flavours.

SPECERIET ⊩○

CLASSIC CUISINE • SIMPLE   Ⓐ/C

Artillerigatan 14 ⊠ 114 51 **PLAN: C2**
Ⓜ Östermalmstorg
TEL. 08-662 30 60 – www.speceriet.se
Closed Christmas, New Year, midsummer, Saturday lunch, Sunday and lunch mid July-mid September
Carte 370/595 SEK

The more casual addendum to the Gastrologik restaurant will get you in the mood for sharing. Sit at communal tables and enjoy the 'dish of the day' at lunchtime or a wider selection of mix and match dishes at dinner.

STUREHOF ⅈO

SEAFOOD • BRASSERIE • FASHIONABLE   🦪 ♿ 🏠 AC 🍽

Stureplan 2 ✉ 114 46 **PLAN: C2**
Ⓜ Östermalmstorg
TEL. 08-440 57 30 – www.sturehof.com
Menu 650 SEK – Carte 265/875 SEK

This bustling city institution dates back over a century and is a wonderful mix of the traditional and the modern. It boasts a buzzing terrace, several marble-topped bars and a superb food court. Classic menus focus on seafood.

SVARTENGRENS ⅈO

MEATS AND GRILLS • FRIENDLY • NEIGHBOURHOOD

Tulegatan 24 ✉ 113 53 **PLAN: B1**
Ⓜ Tekniska Högskolan
TEL. 08-612 65 50 – www.svartengrens.se
Closed Christmas, 31 December and midsummer
Menu 725 SEK – Carte 295/905 SEK (dinner only)

The eponymous chef-owner has created a modern bistro specialising in sustainable meat and veg from producers in the archipelago. Along with smoking and pickling, the dry-aging is done in-house, and the cuts change daily.

VASSA EGGEN 🍴○

MEATS AND GRILLS • FASHIONABLE • RUSTIC

Elite H. Stockholm Plaza • Birger Jarlsgatan 29 ✉ 103 95 PLAN: B1
Ⓜ Östermalmstorg
TEL. 08-216169 – www.vassaeggen.com
Closed midsummer, Christmas, Saturday lunch and Sunday
Menu 550 SEK (lunch) – Carte 445/740 SEK

A pleasant bar leads through to a dimly lit hotel dining room where bold artwork hangs on the walls. Hearty Swedish cooking relies on age-old recipes, with a particular focus on meat; whole beasts are butchered and hung on-site.

GRAND

LUXURY • HISTORIC BUILDING • ELEGANT

Södra Blasieholmshamnen 6 ✉ 103 27 Ⓜ Kungsträdgården PLAN: C2
TEL. 08-679 35 00 – www.grandhotel.se
278 rm ☕ – 🛏 3600/4200 SEK 🛏🛏 4900/5800 SEK – 34 suites
MATHIAS DAHLGREN-MATBAREN ✿,
MATHIAS DAHLGREN-RUTABAGA– See restaurant

The Grand certainly lives up to its name with its Corinthian columns, handsome panelled bar and impressive spa. Classical bedrooms have marble-decked bathrooms and those at the front offer great views over the water to the Old Town. Dining choices include Verandan with its harbour outlook and smörgåsbords, lively Matbaren and vegetarian restaurant Rutabaga.

HOTEL AT SIX

BUSINESS • DESIGN • CONTEMPORARY

Brunkebergstorg 6 ✉ 111 51 PLAN: B2
Ⓜ Kungsträdgården
TEL. 08-578 828 00 – www.hotelatsix.com

343 rm – 👤 2000/3000 SEK 👥 2200/3200 SEK,
🍽 275 SEK – 1 suite

With its laid-back vibe, bold colour scheme, contemporary art collection and 14 metre cocktail bar, this hotel's cool interior couldn't be more of a contrast to its unassuming façade. Bedrooms are monochrome; those on the top floors have panoramic windows. The modern brasserie serves global fare.

NOBIS

HISTORIC • DESIGN • PERSONALISED

Norrmalmstorg 2-4 ✉ 111 86 PLAN: C2
Ⓜ Östermalmstorg
TEL. 08-614 10 00 – www.nobishotel.com

201 rm – 👤 1990/2390 SEK 👥 2890/4590 SEK, 🍽 175 SEK – 1 suite

It started life as two Royal Palaces and later became a bank (the famous 'Stockholm Syndrome' robbery took place here); now it's a smart hotel with two internal courtyards and spacious bedrooms with clean lines, African wood furnishings and marble bathrooms. Dine on modern European cuisine in Noi or globally inspired bistro dishes in Bino, which opens onto the Square.

SHERATON

BUSINESS • CHAIN • MODERN

Tegelbacken 6 ✉ 101 23 PLAN: B2
Ⓜ T-Centralen
TEL. 08-412 36 02 – www.sheratonstockholm.com
465 rm – 🛉 1395/5185 SEK 🛉🛉 1395/5185 SEK, ☕ 259 SEK – 29 suites

This was the first Sheraton to open in Europe, back in 1971, and its unassuming concrete façade is now a listed feature. Bedrooms are smart, spacious and understated; some overlook Lake Mälaren or the Old Town. The lively restaurant offers international buffet lunches and traditional Swedish dinners.

BERNS

HISTORIC BUILDING • BOUTIQUE HOTEL • DESIGN

Näckströmsgatan 8, Berzelii Park ✉ 111 47 PLAN: C2
Ⓜ Kungsträdgården
TEL. 08-566 322 00 – www.berns.se
82 rm – 🛉 1100/3300 SEK 🛉🛉 1280/3500 SEK, ☕ 195 SEK – 6 suites

In 1863 Heinrich Robert Berns opened Stockholm's biggest concert and party hall on this site and, continuing that tradition, events are a big part of this hotel's business. Bedrooms are modern; some have seating areas or balconies. The stunning rococo ballroom offers an extensive Asian fusion menu.

DIPLOMAT

TRADITIONAL • LUXURY • ELEGANT

Strandvägen 7C ⊠ 114 56 PLAN: C2
Ⓜ Kungsträdgården
TEL. 08-459 68 00 – www.diplomathotel.com
130 rm ☕ – 🛏 3275/7975 SEK 🛏🛏 3575/7975 SEK – 3 suites

Early 20C charm combines with modern furnishings in this art nouveau hotel. Take the old cage lift up to the cosy library, which leads through to a sweet little cocktail bar. Elegant bedrooms come in pastel hues and some have harbour views. T Bar (the old tea salon) serves Scandinavian-inspired brasserie dishes.

DOWNTOWN CAMPER BY SCANDIC

BUSINESS • INDUSTRIAL • ECO-FRIENDLY

Brunkebergstorg 9 ⊠ 111 51 PLAN: B2
Ⓜ Kungsträdgården
TEL. 08-517 263 00 – www.scandichotels.com/downtowncamper
494 rm ☕ – 🛏 1100/2000 SEK 🛏🛏 1250/2500 SEK – 9 suites

This unique hotel has an outside living theme: guest areas have urban-chic styling and eco-friendly bedrooms bring the outdoors indoors courtesy of window seats and natural materials. Creatively styled conference rooms come with games; each floor has a table tennis table – and bikes, skateboards and kayaks are available for hire. The brasserie offers comforting fare.

CENTRE

ELITE EDEN PARK

BUSINESS • CONTEMPORARY • MODERN

Sturegatan 22 ⊠ 114 36 PLAN: C1
Ⓜ Östermalmstorg
TEL. 08-555 627 00 – www.elite.se
124 rm ⌷ – 👤 990/2190 SEK 👥 1500/3126 SEK – 1 suite

A smart hotel in a converted office block, designed with the business traveller in mind. Stylish bedrooms boast comfy beds and large showers – some rooms overlook the park and some have small balconies. Choose from an Asian-inspired menu in Miss Voon or British pub dishes in The Bishops Arms.

HAYMARKET BY SCANDIC

BUSINESS • HISTORIC BUILDING • ART DÉCO

Hötorget 13-15 ⊠ 111 57 PLAN: B2
Ⓜ Hötorget
TEL. 08-517 267 00 – www.scandichotels.com/haymarket
401 rm ⌷ – 👤 1400/5000 SEK 👥 1500/6000 SEK – 7 suites

Built in the 1900s, this former department store sits overlooking the Square, just across from the Concert Hall. Greta Garbo once worked here and the décor, particularly in the bedrooms, gives a nod to the art deco style. There's a small movie theatre, a healthy café-cum-bistro, a European restaurant and an American bar which hosts jazz at weekends.

MISS CLARA BY NOBIS

BUSINESS • MODERN • PERSONALISED

Sveavägen 48 ⊠ 111 34 PLAN: B1
Ⓜ Hötorget
TEL. 08-440 67 00 – www.missclarahotel.com
90 rm – ♦ 1490/2790 SEK ♦♦ 1690/3090 SEK, ⚏ 175 SEK – 2 suites

A fashionable hotel in a great location; it used to be a girls' school and its name is that of the former principal. Surprisingly quiet, dark wood bedrooms have good facilities. The atmospheric brasserie offers an international menu with an Italian slant and some classic Swedish specialities.

RADISSON BLU STRAND

BUSINESS • HISTORIC BUILDING • CONTEMPORARY

Nybrokajen 9 box 16396 ⊠ 103 27 PLAN: C2
Ⓜ Kungsträdgården
TEL. 08-506 640 00 – www.radissonblu.com/strandhotel-stockholm
160 rm – ♦ 1295/2695 SEK ♦♦ 1395/3395 SEK, ⚏ 170 SEK – 11 suites

This imposing hotel part-dates from the 1912 Olympics and sits in a lively waterside spot overlooking Nybroviken. Bedrooms are a mix of traditional and modern styles; the Tower Suite boasts a roof terrace with stunning city views. Enjoy a mix of local and global dishes in the airy atrium restaurant.

ETT HEM 🏠

LUXURY • DESIGN • CLASSIC

🛏 🍴 🕸 ⚐

Sköldungagatan 2 ✉ 114 27 PLAN: B1
Ⓜ Tekniska Högskolan
TEL. 08-20 05 90 – www.etthem.se
12 rm ☕ – 🛉 3900/4900 SEK 🛉🛉 3900/9500 SEK

A charming Arts and Crafts townhouse built as a private residence in 1910. It's elegant, understated and makes good use of wood; its name means 'home' and that's exactly how it feels. Bedroom No.6 features an old chimney and No.1 has a four-poster and a huge marble bath. Modern set menus are served in the kitchen, library and orangery.

LYDMAR 🏠

TOWNHOUSE • PERSONALISED • DESIGN

≼ 🍴 ♿ A/C

Södra Blasieholmshamnen 2 ✉ 111 48 PLAN: C2
Ⓜ Kungsträdgården
TEL. 08-22 31 60 – www.lydmar.com
46 rm ☕ – 🛉 2800/3800 SEK 🛉🛉 3100/5200 SEK – 6 suites

Superbly located across the water from the Palace is this charming townhouse; formerly the store for the neighbouring museum's archives. It has a relaxed yet funky vibe and regularly changing contemporary artwork – and the roof terrace with its water feature is a delightful spot come summer. The attractive restaurant offers a modern European brasserie menu.

ELITE H. STOCKHOLM PLAZA

BUSINESS • CHAIN • CONTEMPORARY

彡 と 淑 斗

Birger Jarlsgatan 29 ✉ 103 95 PLAN: B1
Ⓜ Östermalmstorg
TEL. 08-566 220 00 – www.elite.se
143 rm ☒ – 🛉 930/2600 SEK 🛉🛉 1030/3670 SEK – 12 suites
VASSA EGGEN – See restaurant listing

The smaller sister of the Elite Eden Park is found within this attractive, centrally located building with a façade dating from 1884. Bright fabrics stand out against neutral walls in the compact modern bedrooms; go for one of the corner suites.

HOBO

BOUTIQUE HOTEL • UNIQUE • DESIGN

彡 と AC 斗

Brunkebergstorg 4 ✉ 111 51 PLAN: B2
Ⓜ Kungsträdgården
TEL. 08-578 827 00 – www.hobo.se
201 rm – 🛉 900/1700 SEK 🛉🛉 1900/2200 SEK, ☒ 120 SEK

With eco-inspired décor and quirky design features, Hobo offers something a little different. The ground floor exhibits local businesses' work and houses a laid-back bar-lounge serving modern menus. Cleverly designed bedrooms come with headboards that transform into desks and peg board walls hung with gadgets.

KUNGSTRÄDGÅRDEN

TOWNHOUSE • HISTORIC • PERSONALISED

Västra Trädgårdsgatan 11B ✉ 11153 PLAN: B2
Ⓜ Kungsträdgården
TEL. 08-440 66 50 - www.hotelkungstradgarden.se
94 rm - 1450/2950 SEK 1750/3250 SEK

Overlooking the park of the same name is this part-18C building with a classical façade and attractive original features. Bedrooms are individually furnished in a Gustavian-style - it's worth paying the extra for a bigger room. A concise menu of French-inspired dishes is served in the covered courtyard.

RIDDARGATAN

BUSINESS • MODERN • PERSONALISED

Riddargatan 14 ✉ 114 35 PLAN: C2
Ⓜ Östermalmstorg
TEL. 08-555 730 00 - www.ligula.se
78 rm - 995/2995 SEK 1195/3195 SEK - 4 suites

This smart former office block is situated close to the shops and restaurants, and feels very much like a home-from-home. Bedrooms have bold designs and modern wet rooms. The contemporary breakfast room doubles as a lively bar.

TIME

BUSINESS • MODERN • PERSONALISED

♿ ⚒ 👤 🚗

Vanadisvägen 12 ✉ 113 46 PLAN: A1
Ⓜ Odenplan
TEL. 08-545 473 00 – www.timehotel.se
144 rm ☕ – 🛉 1050/2150 SEK 🛉🛉 2050/2550 SEK

This purpose-built business hotel sits in a smart residential area on the edge of town and is run by a friendly, hands-on team. Bedrooms are bright, airy and of a good size; Superiors have Juliet balconies and Studios offer long-term lets.

CLARION COLLECTION
H. WELLINGTON

BUSINESS • TOWNHOUSE • TRADITIONAL

♿ ⚒ 🚗

Storgatan 6 ✉ 114 51 Ⓜ Östermalmstorg PLAN: C1
TEL. 08-667 09 10 – www.wellington.se
Closed 22 December-4 January
61 rm ☕ – 🛉 820/2420 SEK 🛉🛉 1062/3312 SEK – 1 suite

Set in a former office block, this centrally located hotel makes an ideal base for shopping and sightseeing. Simple bedrooms feature bright fabrics and those on the top floor have city views. Buffet dinners are included in the price.

KAGGES 🎭

SWEDISH • FASHIONABLE • COSY

Lilla Nygatan 21 ✉ 111 28 PLAN: C3
🅜 Gamla Stan
– www.kagges.com
Closed first three weeks January, Christmas, midsummer and
Monday-Tuesday
Menu 495 SEK – Carte 300/600 SEK (dinner only)
(booking essential)

This cosy restaurant with a lively buzz is run by two enthusiastic
friends. Ask for a seat at the counter to watch the team prepare
constantly evolving seasonal small plates with plenty of colour and
a Swedish heart. 4 plates per person is about right – or go for the 4
course Chef's Choice of the Day menu.

DJURET 🍴

MEATS AND GRILLS • RUSTIC • NEIGHBOURHOOD   🐾

Lilla Nygatan 5 ✉ 111 28 PLAN: C3
🅜 Gamla Stan
TEL. 08-506 400 84 – www.djuret.se
Closed July, Christmas, New Year, Sunday and Monday
Menu 620 SEK (dinner only) (tasting menu only)
(booking essential)

Various rooms make up this atmospheric restaurant, including one
part-built into the city walls and looking into the impressive wine
cellar. Monthly set menus are formed around 3 key ingredients, and
the masculine cooking has big, bold flavours.

FLICKAN ⭑○

MODERN CUISINE • FASHIONABLE • INTIMATE   Ⓐ/Ⓒ

Yxsmedsgränd 12 ✉ 111 28 **PLAN: C3**
Ⓜ Gamla Stan
TEL. 08-506 400 80 – www.restaurangflickan.se
Closed July, Christmas, New Year and Sunday-Tuesday
Menu 995 SEK (dinner only) (tasting menu only)
(booking essential)

Pass through the busy bar to this small 16-seater restaurant, where
you'll be greeted by a welcoming team. The 13 course set menu keeps
Swedish produce to the fore, and modern dishes have the occasional
Asian or South American twist.

THE FLYING ELK ⭑○

MODERN CUISINE • INN • FRIENDLY

Mälartorget 15 ✉ 111 27 **PLAN: C3**
Ⓜ Gamla Stan
TEL. 08-20 85 83 – www.theflyingelk.se
Closed 24 December, 1 January and midsummer
Carte 400/610 SEK (dinner only)

A good night out is guaranteed at this lively corner spot, which is
modelled on a British pub and has several different bars. Choose
from bar snacks, pub dishes with a twist or a popular tasting menu of
refined modern classics.

PUBOLOGI ⅋○

SWEDISH • COSY • NEIGHBOURHOOD

Stora Nygatan 20 ✉ 111 27 **PLAN: C3**
Ⓜ Gamla Stan
TEL. 08-506 40 086 – www.pubologi.se
Closed July, Christmas, New Year and Sunday-Tuesday
Menu 325 SEK (dinner only) (tasting menu only)

Book a window table at this charming modern bistro for views out over the cobbled street. The 5 course set menu offers refined, rustic dishes; flavours are strong and punchy and seasonality is key. The wine list is impressive.

OAXEN KROG ❀❀

CREATIVE • DESIGN • FRIENDLY

Beckholmsvägen 26 (off Djurgårdsvägen) ✉ 11521 **PLAN: D3**
TEL. 08-551 531 05 – www.oaxen.com
Closed Christmas, New Year, Easter, midsummer, Sunday and Monday
Menu 2100 SEK (dinner only) (booking essential)

Chef:
Magnus Ek

Specialities:
Langoustine, fermented pear, gooseberry, horseradish and juniper. Lamb with hogweed and peas. Unripe strawberries with pineapple weed granité and yoghurt.

A rebuilt boat shed in a delightful waterside location. Diners are led through a door in Oaxen Slip into an oak-furnished room with a slightly nautical feel. Creative, beautifully constructed Nordic dishes are allied to nature and the seasons – they're delicate and balanced but also offer depth of flavour.

OAXEN SLIP 🙂

TRADITIONAL CUISINE • BISTRO   ♿ 🏠 ⟳

Beckholmsvägen 26 (off Djurgårdsvägen) ✉ 115 21 **PLAN: D3**
TEL. 08-55153105 – www.oaxen.com
Closed Christmas and New Year
Menu 395 SEK (weekday lunch) – Carte 400/750 SEK

A bright, bustling bistro next to the old slipway; try for a spot on the delightful terrace. Light floods the room and boats hang from the girders in a nod to the local shipbuilding industry. The food is wholesome and heartening and features plenty of seafood – whole fish dishes are a speciality.

ULLA WINBLADH 🙂

SWEDISH • CLASSIC DÉCOR • COSY   🏠 ⟳

Rosendalsvägen 8 ✉ 115 21 **PLAN: D2**
TEL. 08-534897 01 – www.ullawinbladh.se
Closed 24-25 December
Carte 315/660 SEK (booking essential)

Ulla Winbladh was originally built as a steam bakery for the 1897 Stockholm World Fair and is set in charming parkland beside the Skansen open-air museum. Sit on the terrace or in the older, more characterful part of the building. Hearty Swedish dishes include sweet and sour herring and fish roe.

AT DJURGÅRDEN

POP HOUSE

BOUTIQUE HOTEL • PERSONALISED • MINIMALIST

Djurgårdsvägen 68 ✉ 115 21 PLAN: D2
TEL. 08-502 541 40 - www.pophouse.se
49 rm - 2000/3095 SEK 2000/3295 SEK - 2 suites

Pop House is ideally placed for visitors to the parks and museums of Djurgården. Bypass the queues waiting to enter 'ABBA: The Museum', and head up to one of the spacious, simply furnished bedrooms; most have balconies with pleasant views. The small lounge, bar and restaurant are open-plan.

AT SKEPPSHOLMEN

SKEPPSHOLMEN

HISTORIC • DESIGN • PERSONALISED

Gröna Gången 1 ✉ 111 49 PLAN: D2
TEL. 08-407 23 00 - www.hotelskeppsholmen.se
77 rm - 2290/3090 SEK 2290/3090 SEK - 1 suite

This 17C hotel is perfect for a peaceful stay close to the city. It's set on a small island beside a beautiful park and was built by the king in 1699 for his soldiers (the conference room was once the officers' mess). White bedrooms have a minimalist style and sea or park views. Menus feature Swedish recipes.

BAR AGRIKULTUR 🦗

SWEDISH • COSY • NEIGHBOURHOOD

Skånegatan 79 (by Folkungagatan and Nytorgsgatan) ✉ 116 35
Ⓜ Medborgarplatsen
www.baragrikultur.se
Closed Christmas, Easter and midsummer

Carte 275/435 SEK (dinner only)

The trendy Södermalm district is home to this intimate wine bar,
whose menu lists fresh, tasty small plates which showcase the region's
produce. The three stainless steel tanks contain home-distilled gin
– flavours are changed regularly using various herbs, oils or fruits.
Bookings only taken for early tables.

NOOK 🦗

MODERN CUISINE • INTIMATE • FRIENDLY

Åsögatan 176 ✉ 116 32 PLAN: D3
Ⓜ Medborgarplatsen
TEL. 08-702 12 22 – www.nookrestaurang.se
Closed July, Christmas, Sunday and Monday

Menu 400 SEK (dinner only)

This modern restaurant offers great value. Drop into the bar for Asian-
influenced snacks or head to the intimately lit dining room floor for
one of two set menus. Creative cooking blends Swedish ingredients
with Korean influences; order 3 days ahead for the suckling pig feast.

CAFÉ NIZZA 🍴

SWEDISH • BISTRO • NEIGHBOURHOOD

Åsögatan 171 ✉ 116 32 PLAN: D3
Ⓜ Medborgarplatsen
TEL. 08-640 99 50 – www.cafenizza.se
Closed Christmas and midsummer
Menu 595 SEK – Carte 475/605 SEK (dinner only and Sunday lunch)
(booking essential)

Drop in for a drink and some bar snacks or a 4 course set menu
of unfussy, flavoursome dishes with a mix of Swedish and French
influences. The small room has chequerboard flooring, a granite-
topped bar and a bustling Parisian feel.

FOTOGRAFISKA 🍴

COUNTRY • RUSTIC • DESIGN

Stadsgårdshamnen 22 ✉ 116 45 PLAN: D3
Ⓜ Slussen
TEL. 08-509 005 00 – www.fotografiska.se
Closed July, 24 December, midsummer, Sunday and Monday
Menu 540 SEK – Carte 400/440 SEK (dinner only)

Take in lovely water views from the photography museum. From the
room to the food, there's a green ethos, courtesy of reclaimed wood
and ethical produce. Fresh, flavoursome dishes are largely vegetarian;
go for 1 cold, 2 warm and 1 sweet.

HÄKTET ⅼ⚪

MODERN CUISINE • BISTRO • SIMPLE

Hornsgatan 82 ✉ 118 21 **PLAN: B3**
Ⓜ Zinkensdamn
TEL. 08-84 59 10 – www.haktet.se
Closed 24 and 31 December, 1 January, midsummer Saturday lunch
and Sunday
Carte 395/600 SEK

From 1781-1872 this was a debtors' prison. It has a characterful
courtyard terrace and three bars – one in the style of a speakeasy,
with a secret door. The simple bistro at the back serves classic
Swedish dishes with a modern edge.

ICHI ⅼ⚪

CREATIVE • INTIMATE • TRENDY

Timmermansgatan 38b (via Timmermansgatan)
(South : 0.25km from Mariatorget subway station) ✉ 118 55
Ⓜ Mariatorget
TEL. 08-88 91 30 – www.ichisthlm.se
Closed Christmas-New Year, Easter, 4 weeks in summer and
Sunday-Tuesday
Menu 670 SEK (dinner only) (tasting menu only)

The chef-owner of this intimate little restaurant takes the best
Swedish ingredients and showcases them in creative modern dishes
which are underpinned by Japanese techniques. Sit at the counter
or in front of the open kitchen to make the most of the experience. A
good range of sakes accompanies.

WOODSTOCKHOLM

MODERN CUISINE • BISTRO • NEIGHBOURHOOD

Mosebacke Torg 9 ✉ 116 46 PLAN: C3
Ⓜ Slussen
TEL. 08-36 93 99 – www.woodstockholm.com
Closed Christmas, Sunday and Monday
Menu 565 SEK – Carte 395/610 SEK (dinner only)

A chef-turned-furniture-maker owns this neighbourhood restaurant
overlooking the park. Cooking follows a theme which changes every
2 months and dishes are simple yet full of flavour. In summer, the
private room opens as a wine bar.

RIVAL

BOUTIQUE HOTEL • BUSINESS • PERSONALISED

Mariatorget 3 ✉ 118 91 PLAN: B3
Ⓜ Mariatorget
TEL. 08-545 789 00 – www.rival.se
99 rm ☕ – 🛏 1095/2595 SEK 🛏🛏 1595/4595 SEK – 2 suites

The location is delightful: opposite a beautiful square with gardens
and a fountain. It's owned by ABBA's Benny Andersson and the stylish
bedrooms come with Swedish movie themes and murals of famous
scenes; the 700-seater art deco theatre also hosts regular events and
shows. Dine on global dishes either in the bistro or on the balcony;
the café is popular for snacks.

CLARION H. ARLANDA AIRPORT

BUSINESS • MODERN • ECO-FRIENDLY

Tornvägen 2, Sky City (at Terminals 4-5, 1st floor above street level) ✉ 190 45
TEL. 08-444 18 00 – www.choice.se/clarion/arlandaairport.se
414 rm ⌨ – ♦ 1962/3606 SEK ♦♦ 1962/3606 SEK – 13 suites

A sleek, corporate hotel next to Terminals 4 and 5, with sound eco-credentials – they even collect honey from their own hives. Relax in the large 'Living Room' lounge area or by the outside pool, then have dinner in the bistro which offers a mix of international and Swedish dishes along with runway views.

STALLMÄSTAREGÅRDEN

INN • HISTORIC BUILDING • COSY

Nortull (North: 2 km by Sveavägen) ✉ 113 47
TEL. 08-610 13 00 – www.stallmastaregarden.se
Closed 23-30 December
49 rm ⌨ – ♦ 1101/3120 SEK ♦♦ 1995/3120 SEK – 3 suites

You can enjoy beautiful views over the water to the Royal Park from this brightly painted inn, which dates from the 17C. It comprises several buildings set around a garden courtyard. Cosy bedrooms have a classic style and Oriental touches. Modern Swedish cuisine is influenced by classic Tore Wretman recipes.

VILLA KÄLLHAGEN

TRADITIONAL • BUSINESS • MINIMALIST

⇐ 🐟 🍴 ⛉ 🏛 AC 🛁 P

Djurgårdsbrunnsvägen 10 (East: 3 km by Strandvägen) ✉ 115 27
TEL. 08-665 03 00 – www.kallhagen.se
36 rm ☕ – ♦ 1295/2795 SEK ♦♦ 1495/2995 SEK – 3 suites

This well-run hotel is a popular place for functions, but with its tranquil
waterside location, it's a hit with leisure guests too. Bedrooms feature
four different colour schemes – inspired by the seasons – and have
park or water views. The modern Swedish menu has a classic edge
and comes with wine pairings.

ALOË ❀

CREATIVE • RUSTIC • INTIMATE

Svartlösavägen 52 ✉ 125 33
TEL. 08-556 36 168 – www.aloerestaurant.se
Closed 22 December-March and Sunday-Tuesday

Menu 1600 SEK (dinner only) (surprise menu only)
(booking essential)

Chef:
Niclas Jönsson and Daniel
Höglander

Specialities:
Squid, shimeji and dashi. Autumn
lamb with figs and ras el hanout.
White peach, goat's milk and black
sesame.

Unusually hidden in an old suburban supermarket, this warm,
welcoming restaurant is run by two talented chefs. Snacks at the
kitchen counter are followed by a locally-influenced surprise menu
with a seafood bias. Creative dishes stimulate the senses with their
intense flavours and original combinations.

LUX DAG FÖR DAG ⚑

MODERN CUISINE • BRASSERIE •
NEIGHBOURHOOD

Primusgatan 116 (West: 5.5 km by Norr Mälarstrand) ✉ 112 67
TEL. 08-619 01 90 – www.luxdagfordag.se
Closed 4 weeks July-August, 2 weeks Christmas-New Year, Sunday
and Monday
Menu 650 SEK (dinner) – Carte 300/725 SEK

A bright, modern, brasserie-style restaurant in an old waterside
Electrolux factory dating back to 1916. Generously proportioned
dishes might look modern but they have a traditional base; sourcing
Swedish ingredients is paramount.

BOCKHOLMEN ⚑

SWEDISH • TRADITIONAL DÉCOR •
COUNTRY HOUSE

Bockholmsvägen (Northwest: 7 km by Sveavägen and E18) ✉ 170 78
Ⓜ Bergshamra
TEL. 08-624 22 00 – www.bockholmen.com
Closed 22 December-10 January, midsummer, lunch October-April
and Monday
Carte 425/625 SEK (booking essential)

With charming terraces leading down to the water, and an outside bar,
this 19C summer house is the perfect place to relax on a summer's day.
It's set on a tiny island, so opening times vary. Wide-ranging menus
include weekend brunch.

ULRIKSDALS WÄRDSHUS

TRADITIONAL CUISINE • INN • ROMANTIC

Ulriksdals Slottspark (Northwest: 8 km by Sveavägen and E 18 towards Norrtälje then take first junction for Ulriksdals Slott)
✉ 170 79
Ⓜ Bergshamra
TEL. 08-85 08 15 – www.ulriksdalswardshus.se
Closed Monday
Carte 255/540 SEK (booking essential)

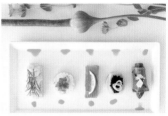

A charming 19C wood-built inn located on the edge of a woodland; start with drinks on the terrace overlooking the lake. Every table in the New England style room has an outlook over the attractive gardens and there's a characterful wine cellar. Classic Swedish dishes are supplemented by a smörgåsbord at lunch.

AT EDSVICKEN

GOTHENBURG

Sweden

D. Schoenen/imageBROKER/age fotostock

Gothenburg is considered to be one of Sweden's friendliest towns, a throwback to its days as a leading trading centre. This is a compact, pretty city whose roots go back four hundred years. It has trams, broad avenues and canals and its centre is boisterous but never feels tourist heavy or overcrowded. Gothenburgers take life at a more leisurely pace than their Stockholm cousins over on the east coast. The mighty shipyards that once dominated the shoreline are now quiet; go to the centre, though, and you find the good-time

ambience of Avenyn, a vivacious thoroughfare full of places in which to shop, eat and drink. But for those still itching for a feel of the heavy industry that once defined the place, there's a Volvo museum sparkling with chrome and shiny steel. The Old Town is the historic heart of the city: its tight grid of streets has grand façades and a fascinating waterfront. Just west is the Vasastan quarter, full of fine National Romantic buildings. Further west again is Haga, an old working-class district which has been gentrified, its cobbled streets sprawling with trendy cafes and boutiques. Adjacent to Haga is the district of Linné, a vibrant area with its elegantly tall 19th century Dutch-inspired buildings. As this is a maritime town, down along the quayside is as good a place to get your bearings as any.

Gothenburg

0   300 m

A   **B**

1

GÖTA ÄLV

Götaälvbron

GÖTA

Göteborgs bron

Mårten

GÖTEBORGS
UTKIKEN

Hamntorget

Stadstjänare-
gatan

GÖTEBORGS
OPERAN

Götaleden

Nils
Ericsons-
platsen

CEN
STA

Nils Ericsonsgatan

FRIHAMNEN

Torggatan

Spannmåls-
gatan

Östra

Nordstads-
torget

Drottning-
torget

Eg

LUNDBYVASSEN

GÖTEBORGS
MARITIMA
CENTRUM

NORDSTADEN

G. Adolfs Torg

BÖRSEN

Hamngatan

▲ Pigalle

2

GÖTEBORGS
STADSMUSEUM

Smedje-gatan

Postgatan
Köpmans-
gatan

Norra

Bhoga ●

Stora

Hamn-kanalen

Hamngatan

H

Kors-
gatan

Drottninggatan

Hamngatan

Södra

Fiskekrogen

▲ Elite Plaza

M

Kyrko-
gatan

Kungsgatan

Dorsia

i Dorsia

Avalon ▲

Kungsports-
platsen

INOM
VALLGRAVEN

Skeppsbron

Magasins-

Västra Hamngatan

Flora ▲

Kungs-
torget

Kun

Kungsgatan

Basargatan

STO
TEAT

KUNGSPARKEN

Hvitfeldts-
platsen

Sahlgrensgatan

kanalen

Allén

Sto

Rosenlundsgatan

Järntorgs-

gatan

FESKEKÖRKA

✚

Nya

Parkgatan

Storgatan

Aschebergs-

P

PUSTERVIK

Norra

Rosenlunds-
Allégatan

Viktoria-

Andréegatan

Södra Allégatan

Masthamnsgatan

Järntorget

gatan

Koka ●

Vasagatan

VASASTAD

Första Långgatan

Linnégatan

Landsvägsgatan

Haga

Nygata

Haga Kyrkogata

Andra Långgatan

HAGA

U

U

Engelbrekts-

Plantagegatan

Lilla Risåsgatan

SKANSEN-
PARKEN

Sp?ngkulls-

U

U

Utsikts-
platsen

U

Tra
La S

Linné-

Veggagatan

Linné-
gatan

SKANSEN
KRONAN

Spisa ●

Övre Husargatan

Föreningsgatan

gatan

Svea-gatan

Risåsgatan

3

A   **B**

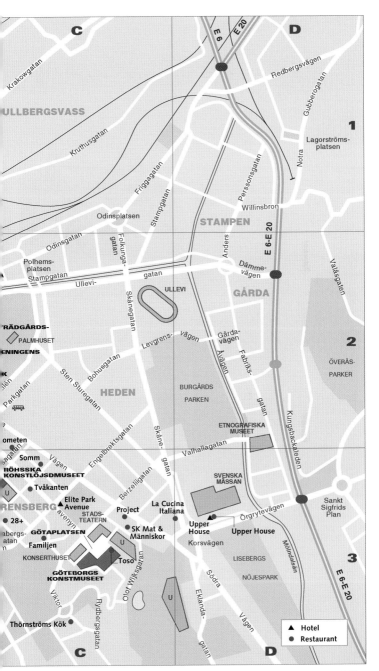

C

Krakowgatan

ULLBERGSVASS

Kruthusgatan

Friggagatan

Stampgatan

Odinsgatan

Odinsplatsen

Polhems-
platsen

Stampgatan

Ullevi-

Folkunga-
gatan

gatan

STAMPEN

Anders

ULLEVI

Skånegatan

Levgrens-

vägen

Dämme-
vägen

GÅRDA

Gårda-
vägen

E 6 - E 20

Willinsbron

Perssonsgatan

Notra

Redbergsvägen

Gubberogatan

1

Lagorströms-
platsen

Valåsgatan

D

E 6   E 20

TRÄDGÅRDS-

◇ **PALMHUSET**

ENINGENS

Parkgatan

Sten Sturegatan

Bohusgatan

HEDEN

BURGÅRDS

PARKEN

Fabriks-

gatan

ETNOGRAFISKA
MUSEET

Valhallagatan

Åvägen

Kungsbackaleden

ÖVERÅS-
PARKER

2

ometen

● **Somm**

Vägen

RÖHSSKA
KONSTLÖJSDMUSEET

● **Tvåkanten**

U

RENSBERG ▲ **Elite Park**
Avenue

avenyn

● **28+**

abergs-
atan

GÖTAPLATSEN

● **Familjen**

KONSERTHUSET

GÖTEBORGS
KONSTMUSEET

● **Thörnströms Kök**

Engelbrektsgatan

Berzeliigatan

Skåne-

gatan

STADS-
TEATERN

● **Project**

● **SK Mat &**
Människor

U

● **Toso**

Olof Wijksgatan

Rydbergsgatan

Viktor

● **La Cucina**
Italiana

Upper
House

Korsvägen

U

SVENSKA
MÄSSAN

Örgrytevägen

Upper House

LISEBERGS

NÖJESPARK

Södra

Ekianda-

Vägen

gatan

Molndalsån

Sankt
Sigfrids
Plan

3

E 6 - E 20

| ▲ | Hotel |
| ● | Restaurant |

C   **D**

BHOGA ✿

CREATIVE • DESIGN • FASHIONABLE

Norra Hamngatan 10 ✉ 411 14 **PLAN: B2**
TEL. 031-13 80 18 – www.bhoga.se
Closed 4-21 August, 22 December-3 January, Sunday and Monday
Menu 600/900 SEK (dinner only) (tasting menu only)

Chef:
Gustav Knutsson

Specialities:
Marinated scallops with kelp, apple and gooseberries. Lamb, ramson, leek and brown butter. Cherries with salted meringue, cream and woodruff.

A chic, contemporary restaurant with an elegant feel; passionately run by two well-travelled friends and their charmingly attentive team. Top quality seasonal ingredients are used in imaginative ways, creating provocative yet harmonious texture and flavour combinations. Wine pairings are original.

KOKA ✿

MODERN CUISINE • DESIGN • NEIGHBOURHOOD A/C

Viktoriagatan 12 ✉ 411 25 **PLAN: B3**
TEL. 031-701 79 79 – www.restaurangkoka.se
Closed 8 July-16 August, Christmas, midsummer and Sunday-Tuesday
Menu 545/945 SEK – Carte 625/715 SEK (dinner only)

Specialities:
Crab with yellow beetroot and quince. Duck breast, goats' curd and pickled spruce shoots. Cherries with bitter almond, potato and butterscotch.

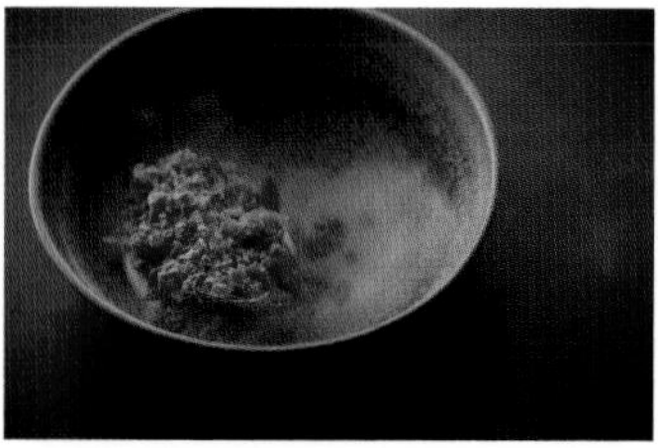

An understatedly elegant room with wooden planks on the floors and walls – and wooden furniture to match. Choose 3, 5 or 7 courses from the set daily menu; dishes are light and refreshingly playful in their approach and fish features highly. Well-chosen wines and smooth service complete the picture.

SK MAT & MÄNNISKOR ✿

MODERN CUISINE • DESIGN • NEIGHBOURHOOD &. A/C

Johannebergsgatan 24 ✉ 412 55 PLAN: C3
TEL. 031-81 25 80 – www.skmat.se
Closed 4 weeks summer, 2 weeks Christmas, Sunday and bank holidays
Menu 650 SEK – Carte 560/605 SEK (dinner only)
(booking essential)

Chef:
Stefan Karlsson

Specialities:
Cured cod with smoked mayonnaise and dried cod roe. Duck with glazed cherries and tarragon. Blueberries, grain-infused cream and crispy buckwheat.

The main focal point of this buzzy restaurant is the 360° open kitchen; not only can you watch the chefs at work but they also deliver your food. The effort put into sourcing and the reverence with which ingredients are treated is commendable and dishes are exciting and packed with flavour.

THÖRNSTRÖMS KÖK ✿

CLASSIC CUISINE • NEIGHBOURHOOD • ROMANTIC 🐕 A/C 🔄

Teknologgatan 3 ✉ 411 32 PLAN: C3
TEL. 031-16 20 66 – www.thornstromskok.com
Closed 6 July-14 August, 22 December-3 January, Easter and Sunday
Menu 675 SEK – Carte 755/905 SEK (dinner only)
(booking essential)

Chef:
Håkan Thörnström

Specialities:
Rabbit with roasted cheese, black truffle and Puy lentils. Turbot with grilled butter sauce and horseradish. Rhubarb and fennel with flaxseed, vanilla and caramel.

An elegant, long-standing restaurant with a stunning wine cave; set in a quiet residential area and run by a welcoming, knowledgeable team. There's a good choice of menus, including 4 different tasting options. Precise, confident, classically based cooking uses top quality produce to create pronounced flavours.

28+ ☼

MODERN CUISINE • ROMANTIC • INTIMATE   ☼ 🄰🄲 ⇔

Götabergsgatan 28 ✉ 411 34 **PLAN: C3**
TEL. 031-20 21 61 – www.28plus.se
Closed 1 July-21 August, Christmas, Sunday and Monday
Menu 895 SEK – Carte 655/705 SEK (dinner only)

Specialities:
Calves' sweetbreads and Jerusalem artichokes. Mirin-glazed haddock with white asparagus. Gateau Marcel with cottage cheese.

This passionately run basement restaurant has been a Gothenburg institution for over 30 years. Modern cooking showcases prime seasonal ingredients, skilfully blending French and Swedish influences to create intricate, flavourful dishes. There's an exceptional cheese selection and an outstanding wine list.

UPPER HOUSE ☼

CREATIVE • ELEGANT • CHIC   ☼ ⇐ ♿ 🄰🄲

Upper House Hotel • Gothia Towers (25th Floor), Mässans gata 24 ✉ 402 26 **PLAN: D3**
TEL. 031-708 82 00 – www.upperhouse.se
Closed 10 July-7 August, 24 December, 1 January, Sunday and Monday

Menu 1400 SEK (dinner only) (surprise menu only)
(booking essential)

Specialities:
Old potatoes and truffle. Plaice, ramson and sturgeon caviar. Selles-sur-Cher cheese and French toast.

A small but very comfortable restaurant with just 6 tables and superb views from its perch on the 25th floor. The single Surprise Menu is made up of numerous elaborate, creative and visually appealing dishes that offer complex layers of flavour. The chefs deliver and explain the dishes themselves.

FAMILJEN 🏮

SCANDINAVIAN • DESIGN • NEIGHBOURHOOD

Arkivgatan 7 ✉ 411 34 **PLAN: C3**
TEL. 031-20 79 79 – www.restaurangfamiljen.se
Closed 24-25 December, midsummer and Sunday
Menu 395/495 SEK – Carte 395/545 SEK (dinner only)
(booking essential)

A lively, friendly eatery divided into three parts: a bar with bench seating and an open kitchen; a bright red room with a characterful cellar and a glass wine cave; and a superb wrap-around terrace. Cooking is good value and portions are generous. There's an appealing wine, beer and cocktail list too.

PROJECT 🏮

MODERN CUISINE • NEIGHBOURHOOD •
FASHIONABLE

Södra vägen 45 ✉ 412 54 **PLAN: C3**
TEL. 031-18 18 58 – www.projectgbg.com
Closed Christmas and Sunday-Tuesday
Menu 400 SEK – Carte 445/565 SEK (dinner only)
(booking essential)

A young couple and their charming service team run this cosy little bistro just outside the city centre. The modern, creative, full-flavoured dishes are Swedish at heart with some global influences; the delicious bread takes 5 days to make and the homemade butter takes 2 days.

SOMM 🏮

MODERN CUISINE • RUSTIC • COSY

Lorensbergsgatan 8 ✉ 411 36 PLAN: C3
TEL. 031-28 28 40 – www.somm.se
Closed July, Christmas, midsummer and Sunday
Menu 395 SEK – Carte 550/645 SEK (dinner only)

A simply but warmly decorated neighbourhood bistro with
contemporary artwork and a cosy, friendly feel. Quality seasonal
ingredients are used to create tasty modern dishes, which feature
on an à la carte and various tasting menus. The wine list offers great
choice and the service is charming and professional.

LA CUCINA ITALIANA 🍴

ITALIAN • INTIMATE • NEIGHBOURHOOD

Skånegatan 33 ✉ 412 52 PLAN: C/D3
TEL. 031-16 63 07 – www.lacucinaitaliana.nu
Closed Christmas, Easter, midsummer, Sunday, Monday and bank
holidays
Menu 460 SEK – Carte 545/635 SEK (dinner only)
(booking essential)

An enthusiastically run restaurant consisting of only 5 tables. Choose
between the à la carte, a daily fixed price menu and a 6 course
surprise tasting 'journey'. The chef-owner regularly travels to Italy
to buy cheeses, meats and wines.

DORSIA ⵏO

MODERN CUISINE • EXOTIC DÉCOR • ROMANTIC 🦂 🛏 A/C 🍽

Dorsia Hotel • Trädgårdsgatan 6 ✉ 411 08 **PLAN: B2**
TEL. 031-790 10 00 – www.dorsia.se
Carte 625/825 SEK

A dramatic hotel dining room split over two levels, with striking flower arrangements, gloriously quirky lighting, and belle époque oil paintings hanging proudly on the walls. Local fish features highly and puddings are worth saving room for. The impressive wine list is rich in burgundies and clarets.

FISKEKROGEN ⵏO

SEAFOOD • ELEGANT • CLASSIC DÉCOR 🦂 A/C 🍽

Lilla Torget 1 ✉ 411 18 **PLAN: B2**
TEL. 031-10 10 05 – www.fiskekrogen.se
Closed 6 July-8 August, Christmas-New Year, midsummer and Sunday
Menu 495 SEK – Carte 435/805 SEK (dinner only and Saturday lunch)

This charming restaurant is set within a 1920s columned Grand Café and showcases top quality seafood in classical dishes; the seafood buffet on Friday and Saturday is impressive. 'Bifångst' offers a tasting menu of modern small plates.

KOMETEN ⅋◯

SWEDISH • TRADITIONAL DÉCOR • NEIGHBOURHOOD 🏠

Vasagatan 58 ✉ 411 37 **PLAN: C2**
TEL. 031-13 79 88 – www.restaurangkometen.se
Closed 23-27 December, 1 January and midsummer

Carte 335/790 SEK (booking essential)

The oldest restaurant in town has a classic façade and a homely, traditional feel; it opened in 1934 and is now part-owned by celebrated chef Leif Mannerström. Sweden's culinary traditions are kept alive here in generous, tasty dishes.

SJÖMAGASINET ⅋◯

SWEDISH • RUSTIC • TRADITIONAL DÉCOR 🏕 ≼ ⅋ 🏠 🖨 🅿

Adolf Edelsvärds gata 5, Klippans Kulturreservat 5 (Southwest: 3.5 km by Andréeg taking Kiel-Klippan exit (Stena Line), or boat from Rosenlund. Also evenings and weekends in summer from Lilla Bommens Hamn) ✉ 414 51
TEL. 031-775 59 20 – www.sjomagasinet.se
Closed 24-30 December, 1-15 January, Saturday lunch and Sunday

Menu 595/925 SEK – Carte 745/1075 SEK

A charming split-level restaurant in an old East India Company warehouse dating from 1775; ask for a table on the upper floor to take in the lovely harbour view. Cooking offers a pleasing mix of classic and modern dishes; lunch sees a concise version of the à la carte and a 3 course set menu.

SPISA ⁑○

MEDITERRANEAN CUISINE • FASHIONABLE • NEIGHBOURHOOD

        ♿ A/C

Övre Husargatan 3 ✉ 411 22 **PLAN: B3**
TEL. 031-386 06 10 – www.spisamatbar.se
Closed 24-25 December, midsummer and Sunday

Menu 375 SEK – Carte 285/515 SEK (dinner only)

A contemporary restaurant set in an up-and-coming area a short walk from the city centre and frequented by a lively, sociable crowd. The menu offers tasty sharing plates with French, Spanish and Italian origins. Try a cocktail too.

TOSO ⁑○

ASIAN • BISTRO • EXOTIC DÉCOR

A/C

Götaplatsen ✉ 412 56 **PLAN: C3**
TEL. 031-787 98 00 – www.toso.nu
Closed Christmas

Carte 300/460 SEK (dinner only)

There's something for everyone at this modern Asian restaurant, where terracotta warriors stand guard and loud music pumps through the air. Dishes mix Chinese and Japanese influences; start with some of the tempting small plates.

TRATTORIA LA STREGA

ITALIAN • FRIENDLY • BISTRO

Aschebergsgatan 23B ✉ 411 27 PLAN: B3
TEL. 031-18 15 01 – www.trattorialastrega.se
Closed 1 July-8 August, 23 December-6 January and Monday

Menu 480 SEK – Carte 280/430 SEK (dinner only)
(booking essential)

A lively little trattoria in a quiet residential area; run by a charming owner. Sit at a candlelit table to enjoy authentic, boldly flavoured Italian cooking and well-chosen wines. Signature dishes include pasta with King crab ragout.

TVÅKANTEN 🍴

TRADITIONAL CUISINE • BRASSERIE • NEIGHBOURHOOD

Kungsportsavenyn 27 ✉ 411 36 PLAN: C3
TEL. 031-18 21 15 – www.tvakanten.se
Closed Christmas, Easter, midsummer and bank holidays

Menu 515 SEK (lunch) – Carte 475/750 SEK

With its welcoming hum and friendly team, it's no wonder this long-standing family-run restaurant is always busy. The dimly-lit, brick-walled dining room is the place to eat. Homely lunches are followed by more ambitious dinners.

VRÅ ⚟

JAPANESE • FASHIONABLE • SIMPLE   ⚟ 🅰🅲

Clarion Hotel Post, Drottningtorget 10 ✉ 411 03   PLAN: C2
TEL. 031-619 06 60 – www.restaurangvra.se
Closed mid-July-mid-August, Christmas, Sunday and Monday
Menu 495/1050 SEK – Carte 335/545 SEK (dinner only)

A cosy, modern hotel restaurant with an open kitchen; run by an
attentive, knowledgeable team. Their tagline is 'Swedish ingredients,
Japanese flavours' and the produce is top quality. Menus include a
set price four courses, and a 'chef's choice' 7 courses.

ELITE PARK AVENUE 🏘

BUSINESS • TRADITIONAL • MODERN

< ⚟ ⚟ 🅸🅵 🅰🅲 ⚟ ⚟

Kungsportsavenyn 36-38 ✉ 400 15   PLAN: C3
TEL. 031-727 10 76 – www.parkavenuecafe.se
317 rm ⚟ – 🛏 1050/2350 SEK 🛏🛏 1250/2750 SEK – 9 suites

Set in a lively location close to many museums and galleries, the
Elite Park Avenue is a popular place for conferences. The interior
is stylish and the bedrooms are spacious and well-equipped – the
rooftop suites come with balconies. Dine in the English pub or on
French or Swedish dishes in the bistro.

ELITE PLAZA

TRADITIONAL • BUSINESS • MODERN

🤸 🏛 🏊 🛌 🚗

Västra Hamngatan 3 ✉ 402 22 **PLAN: B2**
TEL. 031-720 40 40 – www.elite.se
127 rm 🛏 – 🧍 990/2190 SEK 🧍🧍 2600/3900 SEK – 3 suites

This elegant building dates back to the 19C and features ornate ceilings and a Venetian-style sitting room. Bedrooms seamlessly blend the classic and the modern and the service is welcoming and personalised. The restaurant sits within a glass-enclosed courtyard and mixes French and Scandinavian influences.

UPPER HOUSE

LUXURY • BUSINESS • MODERN

⬅ 🤸 ♿ 🛷 🧖 🏛 🏊 🆎 🅿

Gothia Towers, Mässans gata 24 ✉ 402 26 **PLAN: D3**
TEL. 031-708 82 00 – www.upperhouse.se
53 rm 🛏 – 🧍 2290/5790 SEK 🧍🧍 5290/6790 SEK – 1 suite
UPPER HOUSE ✿ – See restaurant listing

Set at the top of one of the Gothia Towers; take in the dramatic view from the terrace or from the lovely three-storey spa. Spacious bedrooms are filled with top electronic equipment and Scandic art – the duplex suites are sublime.

AVALON

BUSINESS • BOUTIQUE HOTEL • DESIGN

Kungstorget 9 ⊠ 411 17 **PLAN: B2**
TEL. 031-751 02 00 – www.avalonhotel.se
101 rm ⌕ – ♦ 1245/2445 SEK ♦♦ 1445/2745 SEK – 3 suites

A boutique hotel in a great location near the shops, theatres and river. Designer bedrooms have the latest mod cons and come with stylish bathrooms; the penthouse suites have balconies. Relax in the rooftop pool then head for the all-day bistro, which opens onto the piazza and serves international cuisine.

DORSIA

TOWNHOUSE • LUXURY • ART DÉCO

Trädgårdsgatan 8 ⊠ 411 08 **PLAN: B2**
TEL. 031-790 10 00 – www.dorsia.se
37 rm ⌕ – ♦ 1990 SEK ♦♦ 2590/6990 SEK
DORSIA – See restaurant listing

Exuberant, eccentric, seductive and possibly a little decadent, this townhouse hotel comes with a theatrical belle époque style, where art from the owner's personal collection, fine fabrics and rich colours add to the joie de vivre. The restaurant is equally vibrant and the atmosphere suitably relaxed.

Avalon • Dejan Sokolovski/Dorsia

EGGERS

TRADITIONAL • LUXURY • ELEGANT

Drottningtorget 2-4 ✉ 411 03 PLAN: B2
TEL. 031-333 44 40 - www.hoteleggers.se
Closed 22-27 December

69 rm - 1220/1925 SEK 2035/2725 SEK

An elegant railway hotel that opened in 1859 with electricity and a telephone in every room. The warm, welcoming interior features old wrought iron, stained glass and period furnishings. The characterful restaurant still has its original wallpaper and offers Swedish and French favourites.

PIGALLE

TOWNHOUSE • FAMILY • VINTAGE

Södra Hamngatan 2A ✉ 411 06 PLAN: B2
TEL. 031-80 29 21 - www.hotelpigalle.se

60 rm - 1000/5000 SEK 1200/5000 SEK - 1 suite

A top-hatted manager will greet you at the reception-cum-welcome-bar of this quirky hotel, which is set within the walls of a historic building. The décor is bold and eclectic, with dramatic features and plenty of personality. In the restaurant you can choose to sit at proper tables or on comfy sofas.

Hotel Eggers • Pigalle

FLORA ⌂

FAMILY • BUSINESS • DESIGN

Grönsakstorget 2 ✉ 411 17 PLAN: B2

TEL. 031-13 86 16 – www.hotelflora.se
Closed Christmas
70 rm ⌂ – ♀ 1120/2400 SEK ♀♀ 1450/2800 SEK

This well-located Victorian mid-terrace is nicely run and has a relaxed, funky feel. Bedrooms benefit from high ceilings; ask for one of the newer, designer rooms. The bar-lounge is a popular spot and doubles as the breakfast room.

VILLAN 🏠

TRADITIONAL • FAMILY • COSY

Sjöportsgatan 2 (West: 6 km by Götaälvbron and Lundbyleden, or boat from Rosenlund) ✉ 417 64
TEL. 031-725 77 77 – www.hotelvillan.com
26 rm ⌂ – ♀ 1200/1900 SEK ♀♀ 1450/2200 SEK

A characterful wood-clad, family-run house; once home to a shipbuilding manager and later floated over to this location. The stylish interior has smart, clean lines. Contemporary bedrooms boast good mod cons – No.31 has a sauna and a TV in the bathroom. The first floor restaurant overlooks the river.

Lelle Anderzén/Flora - Flora • Villan

LANDVETTER AIRPORT HOTEL

BUSINESS • FAMILY • DESIGN

Flygets Hotellväg (East: 30 km by Rd 40) ✉ 438 13
TEL. 031-97 75 50 – www.landvetterairporthotel.com
187 rm ☕ – 👤 1595/1795 SEK 👥 1695/1895 SEK – 1 suite

A family-run hotel located just minutes from the airport terminal. The light, open interior has a calm air and a fresh Scandic style, and bedrooms have an unfussy retro feel. The informal restaurant offers a mix of Swedish and global dishes, along with a BBQ and grill menu at dinner.

MALMÖ

Sweden

secablue/iStock

Malmö was founded in the 13C under Danish rule and it wasn't until 1658 that it entered Swedish possession and subsequently established itself as one of the world's biggest shipyards. The building of the 8km long Oresund Bridge in 2000 reconnected the city with Denmark and a year later, the Turning Torso apartment block was built in the old shipyard district, opening up the city to the waterfront. Once an industrial hub, this 'city of knowledge' has impressively green credentials: buses run on natural gas and there are

400km of bike lanes. There's plenty of green space too; you can picnic in Kungsparken or Slottsparken, sit by the lakes in Pildammsparken or pet the farm animals in 'Folkets'. At the heart of this vibrant city lie three squares: Gustav Adolfs Torg, Stortorget and Lilla Torg, connected by a pedestrianised shopping street. You'll find some of Malmö's oldest buildings in Lilla Torg, along with bustling open-air brasseries; to the west is Scandinavia's oldest surviving Renaissance castle and its beautiful gardens – and beyond that, the 2km Ribersborg Beach with its open-air baths. North is Gamla Väster with its charming houses and galleries, while south is Davidshall, filled with designer boutiques and chic eateries. Further south is Möllevångstorget, home to a throng of reasonably priced Asian and Middle Eastern shops.

VOLLMERS ✿✿

CREATIVE • ELEGANT • INTIMATE

Tegelgårdsgatan 5 ⊠ 21133 PLAN: E2
TEL. 040-57 97 50 – www.vollmers.nu
Closed Christmas, Sunday and Monday

Menu 1600 SEK (dinner only) (tasting menu only)
(booking essential)

Chef:
Mats Vollmer

Specialities:
Duck, spring onion and havgus
cheese. Salsify with buttermilk and
cress. Raspberry, cream and violet.

An intimate restaurant with charming, professional service, set in a
pretty 19C townhouse. The talented Mats Vollmer showcases some
of the area's finest seasonal ingredients in a set 8 course menu of
intricate and elaborate modern dishes, which are innovative, perfectly
balanced and full of flavour.

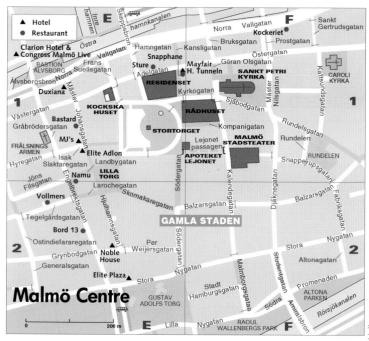

BLOOM IN THE PARK ✿

CREATIVE • DESIGN • CHIC ♿ 🛱 A/C

Pildammsvägen 17
(Southwest : 2 km.by Stora Nygatan and Fersens väg) ✉ 214 66
TEL. 040-793 63 – www.bloominthepark.se
Closed 24 December, 1 January, Easter, Sunday and bank holidays
Menu 495/695 SEK (dinner only) (surprise menu only)

Specialities:
Cod, wasabi, peas and grapefruit.
Variations of lamb with cabbage,
truffle and walnuts. Chocolate,
Sichuan pepper, passion fruit and
white chocolate.

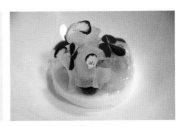

A delightful lakeside lodge with a waterside terrace for drinks; run
by an ebullient owner. There is no written menu or wine list; instead,
the kitchen prepares a balanced set meal of modern dishes with
international influences, which are accompanied by thoughtfully
paired wines.

SAV ✿

CREATIVE • COSY • RUSTIC 🛏 🅿

Vindåkravägen 3, Tygelsjö (South: 10.5 km by Trelleborgsvägen
E22/E6) ✉ 21875
TEL. 072-022 85 20 – www.savrestaurang.nu
Closed 24 December-8 January, 17-20 April, 21 June-6 August,
Sunday-Tuesday
Menu 625/895 SEK (dinner only) (surprise menu only)
(booking essential)

Chef:
Sven Jensen and Alexander Fohlin
Specialities:
Celery, pine spruce, unripe currants
and hazelnut. Beef with yeast, dill
and blackcurrant. Wild blueberry
with hay and pine syrup.

Flickering candles and crackling fires provide a warm welcome at
this charming 19C farmhouse. The two young chefs pick many of the
ingredients and explain their surprise menu personally. Dishes belie
their apparent simplicity – inspired combinations of tastes, textures
and temperatures all play their part.

Eric Lindqvist/Bloom in the Park • Erik Putsep/SAV

BASTARD 😀

MODERN CUISINE • SIMPLE • TRENDY

Mäster Johansgatan 11 ✉ 211 21 PLAN: E1
TEL. 040-12 13 18 – www.bastardrestaurant.se
Closed 25 December, Easter, midsummer, Sunday and Monday
Menu 395 SEK – Carte 305/510 SEK (dinner only)

Popular with the locals, this is a bustling venue with an edgy, urban vibe. Style-wise, schoolroom meets old-fashioned butcher's, with vintage wood furniture, tiled walls, moody lighting and an open kitchen. Small plates offer nose-to-tail eating with bold, earthy flavours; start with a 'Bastard Plank' to share.

NAMU 😀

KOREAN • FRIENDLY • SIMPLE

Landbygatan 5 ✉ 21134 PLAN: E1/2
TEL. 040-12 14 90 – www.namu.nu
Closed Christmas, 31 December-1 January, Sunday and Monday
Menu 395/595 SEK (dinner) – Carte 375/570 SEK

Colourful, zingy food from a past Swedish MasterChef winner blends authentic Korean flavours with a modern Scandinavian touch. Dishes are satisfying – particularly the fortifying ramen – and desserts are more than an afterthought. Cookbooks line the shelves and friendly service adds to the lively atmosphere.

ATMOSFÄR ⫯○

SWEDISH • NEIGHBOURHOOD   ♿ 🚉 AC ⇔

Fersens väg 4 (Southwest : 1 km. by Regementsgatan) ✉ 211 42
TEL. 040-12 50 77 – www.atmosfar.com
Closed Christmas, midsummer, Saturday lunch and Sunday
Menu 330 SEK (dinner) – Carte 350/500 SEK

A formal yet relaxed eatery on the main road; dine at the bar, in the restaurant or on the pavement terrace. The menu consists of small plates, of which three or four should suffice. Fresh Skåne cooking is delivered with a light touch.

B.A.R. ⫯○

MODERN CUISINE • WINE BAR • NEIGHBOURHOOD   🚉 ⇔

Erik Dahlbersgatan 3
(Southwest : 1 km by Gustav Adolfs torg and Torggatan) ✉ 211 48
TEL. 040-17 01 75 – www.barmalmo.se
Closed Easter, Christmas, Sunday and Monday
Menu 450 SEK – Carte 275/415 SEK (dinner only)

This lively wine-bar-cum-restaurant in trendy Davidshall is named after its owners, Besnick And Robert. The interesting menu tends towards the experimental; expect dishes like Jerusalem artichoke ice cream with hazelnut mayo.

BISTRO STELLA ¶○

MODERN CUISINE • NEIGHBOURHOOD • PUB

Linnégatan 25, Limhamn (Southwest: 7 km by Limhamnsvägen: bus 4 from Central station) ✉ 216 12
TEL. 040-15 60 40 – www.bistrostella.se
Closed Christmas, midsummer, Sunday and Monday
Menu 395 SEK – Carte 310/790 SEK (dinner only)

A lively gastropub in a residential area not far from the Øresund Bridge. Its bright, cosy bar sits between two dining rooms and its menu features pub dishes like burgers, fish and chips and charcuterie platters. Cooking is rustic and tasty.

BORD 13 ¶○

CREATIVE • WINE BAR • FRIENDLY

Engelbrektsg 13 ✉ 211 33 PLAN: E2
TEL. 042-587 88 – www.bord13.se
Closed Christmas, Easter, midsummer, Sunday and Monday
Menu 350/650 SEK (dinner only) (tasting menu only)

Sister to B.A.R. restaurant, is the bright, spacious and stylish 'Table 13', which offers a set 3 or 6 course menu and a diverse selection of biodynamic wines. Original Nordic cooking has some interesting texture and flavour combinations.

Bistro Stella • Michelin

KOCKERIET ⑩

MODERN CUISINE • RUSTIC • INTIMATE

Norra Vallgatan 28 ✉ 211 25 **PLAN: F1**
TEL. 040-796 06 – www.kockeriet.se
Closed 24-25 and 31 December, 1 January, Easter, midsummer and
Sunday
Menu 645/795 SEK (dinner only) (tasting menu only)

Well-known TV chef Tariq Taylor uses this characterful timbered 17C
grain warehouse to deliver his own brand of modern cuisine, founded
on ingredients from his kitchen garden and his worldly travels. Menus
take on a tasting format. The beef from the on-view aging cabinets
is particularly good.

MRS BROWN ⑩

TRADITIONAL CUISINE • WINE BAR • TRENDY

Storgatan 26
(Southwest : 1 km. by Amiralsgatan) ✉ 211 42
TEL. 040-97 22 50 – www.mrsbrown.se
Closed Easter, 24 December and Sunday
Carte 380/460 SEK (dinner only and Saturday lunch)

This retro brasserie's bar opens at 3pm for drinks and nibbles, while
the kitchen opens at 6pm. Make sure you try one of the cocktails. Well-
presented unfussy cooking has a modern edge and showcases the
region's ingredients.

Carin Palsson/Kockeriet • Mrs Brown

MUTANTUR 🍴○

MODERN CUISINE • FASHIONABLE • NEIGHBOURHOOD 🄰🄲

Erik Dahlbergsgatan 12-14 (Southwest : 1 km. by Gustav Adolfs torg
and Torggatan) ✉ 211 42
TEL. 076-101 72 05 – www.restaurantmutantur.se
Closed 3 weeks midsummer, 23-26 and 30-31 December,
1-2 January, Saturday and Sunday

Carte 350/550 SEK (dinner only) (bookings not accepted)

Semi-industrial styling means concrete floors, brick-faced walls and
exposed ducting; there's also an open kitchen and counter dining. The
extensive menu offers snacks and small plates with a Nordic style and
some Asian influences; they recommend between 3 and 5 per person.

SNAPPHANE 🍴○

MODERN CUISINE • TRENDY • INTIMATE   🄰🄲 🐾

Mayfair Hotel Tunneln • Adelgatan 4 ✉ 211 22 PLAN: E1
TEL. 040-15 01 00 – www.snapphane.nu
Closed 22-26 December, 1 January, Easter and Sunday

Menu 595 SEK – Carte 415/615 SEK (dinner only)
(booking essential)

An elegant, intimate bistro with an open-plan kitchen at its centre.
Innovative modern cooking uses top quality ingredients and dishes
are well-presented, well-balanced and full of flavour. Service is
friendly and professional.

STURE ⑪○

FRENCH • FRIENDLY • NEIGHBOURHOOD

Adelgatan 13 ⊠ 21122 PLAN: E1
TEL. 040-12 12 53 – www.restaurantsture.com
Closed July, 22-30 December, Sunday and Monday
Menu 950/1195 SEK (dinner only) (tasting menu only)

A landmark in the city, this elegant 19C townhouse started life as a
cinema and has been a restaurant for over 100 years. Its original glass-
panelled ceiling is a great feature. Modern cooking blends French and
Nordic influences – choose from 7 monthly changing dishes. Service
is enthusiastic.

CLARION H. AND CONGRESS
MALMÖ LIVE

BUSINESS • MODERN • FUNCTIONAL

Dag Hammarskjölds Torg 2 ⊠ 211 18 PLAN: E1
TEL. 040-20 75 00 – www.clarionlive.se
444 rm ⌂ – ♦ 900/2500 SEK ♦♦ 1100/2700 SEK – 2 suites

The city's second tallest building affords a superb 360° view of the
city; choose a bedroom on an upper floor for a view of the Øresund
Bridge and Denmark. Kitchen & Table's eclectic menu combines
American classics and international influences and you can enjoy a
cocktail in the adjoining Skybar. The Ground floor houses an informal
Mexican-themed restaurant and bar.

MJ'S

BUSINESS • MODERN • PERSONALISED

Mäster Johangatan 13 ✉ 211 21 PLAN: E1
TEL. 040-664 64 00 – www.mjs.life
68 rm ☺ – ♦ 695/1895 SEK ♦♦ 795/2495 SEK – 10 suites

A centrally located hotel, just off the main square, with a relaxed and peaceful air. Stylish, well-proportioned bedrooms have luxurious touches. Enjoy a locally sourced organic breakfast under the atrium's glass roof.

ELITE ADLON

BUSINESS • CHAIN • MODERN

Mäster Johansgatan 15 ✉ 211 21 PLAN: E1
TEL. 040-24 85 00 – www.elite.se
128 rm ☺ – ♦ 995/2195 SEK ♦♦ 1046/2345 SEK – 1 suite

A smart hotel on the site of the city's original food market: beamed ceilings and iron columns bring character to the modern interior. Bright, well-equipped bedrooms are quiet considering the hotel's location. There's a colourful bar and a simply furnished restaurant; modern dishes are created using local produce.

ELITE PLAZA

BUSINESS • CHAIN • MODERN

Gustav Adolfs torg 49 ✉ 211 39 PLAN: E2
TEL. 040-664 48 71 - www.elite.se
116 rm - 977/2372 SEK 1100/2712 SEK - 1 suite

Behind the wonderful period façade is a smart, up-to-date corporate hotel. Modern bedrooms are a good size: the best look onto a pretty square; the quietest overlook the inner courtyard. The British-themed bar has a pleasant pavement terrace.

STORY STUDIO MALMÖ

CHAIN • BUSINESS • PERSONALISED

Tyfongatan 1 (Northwest : 1.25 km. by Kalendegatan) ✉ 211 19
TEL. 040-616 52 00 - www.storyhotels.com
Closed 23-25 December
95 rm - 890/2590 SEK 890/2590 SEK

The modern, well-equipped bedrooms of this hotel are situated on the top 5 floors of a 14 storey building next to the old port, and feature floor to ceiling windows. The rooftop restaurant serves Japanese dishes accompanied by beautiful city and harbour views.

Linda Broström/Elite Plaza • Michelin

CENTRE

DUXIANA

TOWNHOUSE · DESIGN · CONTEMPORARY

分 & AC

Mäster Johansgatan 1 ✉ 211 21 PLAN: E1
TEL. 040-607 70 00 – www.malmo.hotelduxiana.com
22 rm ☲ – ♦ 1390/1490 SEK ♦♦ 1690/2590 SEK

A well-located boutique hotel; owned by the Dux bed company, who
unusually use part of the lobby to showcase their products! Chic,
contemporary bedrooms range from compact singles to elegant junior
suites with a bath in the room. Staff are friendly and professional.
Modern Swedish dishes are served at lunch.

MAYFAIR H. TUNNELN

TOWNHOUSE · HISTORIC · PERSONALISED

分 🏊

Adelgatan 4 ✉ 211 22 PLAN: E1
TEL. 040-10 16 20 – www.mayfairhotel.se
81 rm ☲ – ♦ 800/1900 SEK ♦♦ 1725/2200 SEK
SNAPPHANE – See restaurant listing

An imposing early 17C property steeped in history. Some of the
homely, spotlessly kept bedrooms have spa baths. Breakfast is served
in the impressive vaulted cellars dating back to 1307 and you can
enjoy a complimentary coffee in the classical lounge. Snapphane
showcases the latest local, organic ingredients.

Duxiana • Mayfair H. Tunneln

MORE

TOWNHOUSE • BUSINESS • MODERN

Norra Skolgatan 24 (South : 1.25 km. by Kaptensgatan) ✉ 214 22
TEL. 040-6551000 – www.themorehotel.com
68 rm ☕ – ♦ 895/1695 SEK ♦♦ 1095/2695 SEK

A striking aparthotel converted from a late 19C chocolate factory. The studios are modern and extremely spacious, with kitchenettes, sofa beds and light loft-style living areas. They are let on a nightly basis but are ideal for longer stays.

PARK INN BY RADISSON MALMÖ

CHAIN • FUNCTIONAL • MODERN

Sjömansgatan 2 (Northwest : 2.25 km. by Norra Neptunigatan) ✉ 211 19
TEL. 040-6286000 – www.parkinn.com/hotel-malmo
231 rm ☕ – ♦ 795/1395 SEK ♦♦ 795/1395 SEK

A good value hotel, well-situated on the Western Harbour beside the World Trade Centre and the Västra Hamnen waterfront. Bedrooms are spacious and well-equipped; the business rooms on the higher floors come with robes and have better views. The Bar & Grill offers easy dining.

CENTRE

NOBLE HOUSE

BUSINESS • FAMILY • FUNCTIONAL

🏠 ♿ 🔥 🛋 🚗

Per Weijersgatan 6 ✉ 21134 **PLAN: E2**
TEL. 040-664 30 00 – www.hotelnoblehouse.se
137 rm ☕ – 🚹 795/1550 SEK 🚻 895/1750 SEK – 2 suites

A centrally located hotel, close to the bus station. Classically
furnished, well-equipped bedrooms offer good value for money; ask
for a room on one of the upper floors. There's a cosy lounge and a
modern restaurant which serves traditional Swedish dishes.

GOTLAND

KRAKAS KROG 🍴

CREATIVE • RUSTIC • COSY   🔸 🛎 🏠 **P**

Kräklings 223, Katthammarsvik (Southeast: 39 km by 143 on
146) ✉ 623 70
TEL. 0498-530 62 – www.krakas.se
Closed 1 October-1 June and Monday-Wednesday

Menu 575/1050 SEK (dinner only and Saturday lunch)
(booking essential)

An appealing countryside restaurant with a veranda overlooking the
garden and a relaxed, homely ambience; its charming owner boasts
an impressive knowledge of wine. Creative cooking utilises the best of
Gotland's seasonal ingredients; flavours are intense and combinations
stimulating and well-judged. Simple, stylish bedrooms complete the
picture.

FÄVIKEN MAGASINET ❀❀

CREATIVE • INTIMATE • RUSTIC

Fäviken 216 ✉ 837 94
TEL. 0647-40177 – www.favikenmagasinet.se
Closed 25 December-2 January, 20-21 April, Sunday and Monday

Menu 3000 SEK (dinner only) (surprise menu only)
(booking essential)

Chef:
Magnus Nilsson

Specialities:
Swiss chard, oat sauce and rhubarb.
Steamed perch with perch garum
butter. Aged apple and moulded
milk.

This remote yet idyllically set hunting estate offers a truly unique
experience. The team hunts, forages, grows and preserves – and
this bounty is put to stunning use in the multi-course dinner, using
techniques rooted in Scandic traditions. All guests are served at the
same time, by the chefs themselves. Bedrooms offer simple, rustic
comforts.

BRASSERIE 1742 ⑩

FRENCH • DESIGN • FASHIONABLE

Stora vägen 75 ✉ 365 43
TEL. 0478-348 30 – www.kostabodaarthotel.se
Closed Sunday-Tuesday

Menu 650/895 SEK (dinner only) (tasting menu only)
(booking essential)

A little more formal than its name suggests; enjoy creative snacks and
an aperitif by an impressive indoor firepit before descending into the
cellar-like restaurant. Accomplished French cooking uses luxurious
ingredients in classic flavour combinations, with modern presentation
and a playful edge.

KOSTA BODA ART

BUSINESS • DESIGN • CONTEMPORARY

🌿 ♿ 🛋 🖼 💆 🏊 🧖 AC ⬆️ 🏌️ P

Stora vägen 75 ✉ 365 43
TEL. 0478-348 30 – www.kostabodaarthotel.se
102 rm ⌚ – 🚹 1200/2000 SEK 🚺 1850/4500 SEK
BRASSERIE 1742 – See restaurant listing

Kosta is renowned for its glassworks and this stylish hotel which sits at its centre showcases some stunning glass sculptures, all of which are for sale. Each of the stylish bedrooms is decorated with pieces from one of 7 renowned artists, as is the impressive cocktail bar.

DANIEL BERLIN 😊😊

CREATIVE • FRIENDLY • INTIMATE

🛏 ♿ P

Diligensvägen 21 ✉ 273 92
TEL. 0417-203 00 – www.danielberlin.se
Closed 22 December-31 January, 16-25 June, 27 July-13 August, Sunday-Monday, lunch Tuesday-Wednesday, and except 26 June-25 July, Tuesday dinner and Thursday-Friday lunch
Menu 1150/1950 SEK (surprise menu only) (booking essential)

Chef:
Daniel Berlin
Specialities:
Chicken livers with Linderöd pork. Celeriac and cod. Egg whites with berries and fruit from the garden.

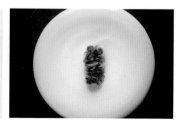

A delightful 150 year old building in a quiet hamlet houses this charmingly run little restaurant. The highly skilled kitchen mixes New Nordic elements with a classic base to make the most of truly luxurious ingredients. There's a purity and subtlety to the 20+ dishes and the contrast in textures is memorable.

PM & VÄNNER ✿

CREATIVE • ELEGANT • INTIMATE

PM & Vänner Hotel • Storgatan 22 ✉ 352 31
TEL. 0470-75 97 10 – www.pmhotel.se
Closed 8 weeks summer, Christmas, New Year and Sunday-Wednesday
Menu 895/1495 SEK (dinner only) (tasting menu only)
(booking essential)

Specialities:
Crayfish from Lake Örken with carrot and dill. Duck breast from Söderslätt with lavender, beetroots and plums. Blackberries from Värend.

A formal hotel restaurant serving a 5 or 9 course set menu of sophisticated, original modern Nordic dishes. Their philosophy is based on 'forest, lake and meadow', and most of the ingredients come from surrounding Småland. An extraordinary wine list offers a huge array of vintages from top producers.

PM & VÄNNER

BUSINESS • LUXURY • DESIGN

Västergatan 10 ✉ 352 31
TEL. 0470-75 97 00 – www.pmhotel.se
74 rm ⌂ – ♦ 1690 SEK ♦♦ 1990 SEK – 1 suite
PM & VÄNNER ✿ – See restaurant listing

A well-run, very stylish hotel with great facilities, including a bakery, a florist and a spa, as well as an appealing roof terrace complete with a bar, lounge, hot tub and plunge pool. Spacious, stark white bedrooms come with ultra-comfy beds and bespoke toiletries. The buzzy Bistro has a large terrace.

INDEX

INDEX OF...
RESTAURANTS

G

H

I

J

K

V

W

Oaxen Slip, Stockholm

INDEX OF...
HOTELS